GP RECRUITMENT
STAGE 2

SJTs for
GPST / GPVTS
Shortlisting

Situational Judgement Tests
Professional Dilemmas

Author: Olivier Picard BSc MSc

1

Published by ISC Medical
Suite 434, Hamilton House, Mabledon Place, London WC1H 9BB
www.iscmedical.co.uk - Tel: 0845 226 9487

First edition (published in electronic form): December 2006
Second edition: October 2007

ISBN13: 978-1-905812-13-4
A catalogue record for this book is available from the British Library.

TABLE OF CONTENTS

ISCMEDICAL
Interview Skills Consulting

Section 1

Introduction

What are Situational Judgement Tests?

Situational Judgement Tests (SJTs) – also called Professional Dilemmas – are a tool used in many industries to assess your ability to use your judgement in resolving problems in a work-related situation. They are designed to test generic competencies as opposed to clinical or technical skills and therefore a good dose of common sense is required instead of strong clinical knowledge (which is tested through other means such as MCQs/EMQs). The competencies tested are well known as they appear in the National Person Specification for the GP selection process. They effectively match those qualities required of any good doctor and should not be a surprise to you. They include:

- **Empathy & Sensitivity**
  Your ability to take on board other people's perspectives and to handle other people, whether patients or colleagues, with care, attention and understanding.

- **Communication Skills**
  Your ability to adjust the way you behave and communicate to the requirements of different situations.

- **Conceptual Thinking & Problem Solving**
  Your ability to think laterally and forward, to analyse situations, and plan the most appropriate response.

- **Coping with Pressure**
  Your ability to recognise your own limitations and deal with pressure and stress by developing appropriate coping mechanisms.

- **Organisation & Planning**
  Your ability to analyse, retain, use and organise information, people and time effectively. Your ability to plan all resources to achieve a desired result.

- **Managing Others & Team Involvement**
  Your ability to work effectively with others.

- **Professional Integrity**
  Your willingness to take responsibility for your own actions and to respect others.

- **Learning & Personal Development**
  Your willingness to learn from experience and constantly update your skills and knowledge.

The full National Person Specification can be found on the national GP recruitment website at http://www.gprecruitment.org.uk.

Two styles of SJT questions
SJT questions usually come in two distinct formats, both of which are used in the GPST selection paper.

- *Type 1: Ranking possible actions*
  You are given a scenario which highlights a particular problem or dilemma. The question sets out four or five possible actions that you may envisage taking. Your task is to rank these options from the most suitable to the least suitable.

- *Type 2: Selecting multiple appropriate actions*
  You are given a scenario which highlights a particular problem or dilemma. The question sets out a large number of options (typically seven). Out of the list, you must pick the three actions that you deem most suitable. There is no need to rank them in any particular order.

See Section 2 for worked examples of each type of SJT question.

Answering the questions
All questions must be answered from the perspective of a junior trainee doctor. Typically the SJT paper will contain 50 questions that you will need to answer in 90 minutes. This makes it an average of 1 minute 48 seconds per question. Although this seems a lot at first glance, in reality many people run out of time, not least because the scenarios and possible options take some time to read, but also because each question requires a degree of analysis which may take

you well beyond the average allocated time. In many ways, SJT questions are testing your instinctive reactions and therefore favour those candidates who naturally match the desired criteria for entry into General Practice – after all, this is the primary aim the examiners are seeking to reach. Nevertheless, with a little practice, everyone can gain an understanding of how the questions are structured and the level of answer required.

Marking SJT questions

Unlike MCQs or EMQs, where there is one correct answer that you must find in order to score, the marking of SJT questions is done in relation to the distance between your answer and the "benchmark" answer specified by the examiners. In simple terms, you will score the maximum possible mark if your answer matches the benchmark answer exactly. However, if your answer is slightly different (e.g. two options are ranked differently) then you may still score marks (albeit fewer).

This marking system reflects the fact that, although there is an ideal answer, in many cases it would not be totally wrong to take a slightly different approach. It therefore offers more flexibility and helps distinguish between the candidates who got it totally wrong and those who are not far away from the desired final answer. It should be noted, however, that, although small deviations can be rewarded by partial marks, more substantial deviations from the benchmark answer are likely to attract a "nil" mark. In addition, the marking schedule may have compulsory ranking requirements, i.e. you must rank some specific options as first or last otherwise you score "nil" regardless of how close you were to the benchmark answer on the other options. In any case, your aim should be to match the benchmark answer exactly in order to maximise your personal score.

In this book you will find:
- 2 worked examples (one for each type of SJT question)
- 52 practice scenarios dealing with a wide range of dilemmas
- Fully explained answers for all scenarios.

Good luck with your preparation.

Olivier Picard

Section 2

Worked examples

WORKED EXAMPLE 1

You have just finished a long 12-hour medical take and you are feeling washed out. You need to send an application form for your next post by tomorrow and you realise far too late that it will take you a good 5 hours to complete it. It is already midnight and you have a busy shift tomorrow which starts at 8am. What do you do?

Rank each of the following options from 1 to 5
(1= Most appropriate; 5= Least appropriate):
A. Forget the application form. There is nothing that you can do about it.
B. Call your Registrar first thing in the morning to see if you can get some time off to finish the form. You can then go to work in the afternoon.
C. Complete the form until 5am and then go to work at 8am.
D. Copy the answers from a form that your friend did last year and which got him through.
E. Call in sick the next morning and do the form properly.

Suggested answer: 1:B – 2:A – 3:E – 4:C – 5:D

How to approach this question
Option A seems a sensible approach but then you will lose out (admittedly by your own fault, but there may be a way around it).

Option B seems sensible too. You are involving your senior. You are taking a gamble because he might refuse but if he does then you will be no worse off than under option A anyway. At least you will have tried to find a solution by using the appropriate channels. This shows good insight and also a good approach to team work.

Option C would only give you 3 hours' sleep and would be unsafe.
Option D is plagiarism.
Option E would be lying and is therefore dishonest.

From this you can deduce the following:

- A and B are the two most sensible options with B being better than A because it may achieve the desired result in the most acceptable manner. A is just giving up when there may be an alternative which would satisfy most people.

- There is a grey area with C and E. Staying up late when you are already tired and then going in with little sleep could be potentially dangerous for patients. On the other hand, lying is also unacceptable. Faced with two bad options you must think about the consequences of both. Going to work whilst tired may be fatal for a patient. In addition, your team will be relying on you to be fully performing when you may not be. On the other hand, lying may look bad but at least you are not compromising patient safety. Also, if you call in sick, you are giving your team an opportunity to organise itself around your absence and to optimise patient care. In conclusion, neither C nor E are really acceptable but E must be better than C purely on the grounds of patient safety. You might be forgiven for lying to your team but you risk being struck off for placing a patient in danger.

We have now identified that B and A are the top two options in that order and that E and C are two of the bottom options in that order. This gives us the sequence B – A – E – C. The only outstanding issue is where D should fit.

Option D is a grave offence which would potentially be punished by being struck off the Register. No excuse that you could give would justify your behaviour. Option C as discussed earlier is potentially unsafe, with the emphasis being on the word "potentially": provided you remain alert and recognise a situation when you have become unsafe, then it may just about be acceptable (and you still retain the option to go home later if you are too tired). Therefore D must be worse than C.

WORKED EXAMPLE 2

During a very busy shift, the relatives of a recently deceased patient want to see you to discuss "things". What do you do?

Choose the three most appropriate actions to take in this situation:

A. Ask the nurse to talk to the relatives to get an understanding of the type of "things" that they want to discuss so that you can be fully prepared when you see them.

B. Tell the nurse to let the relatives know that you are aware they are waiting, that you are busy right now but that if they go home you will call them as soon as you are free.

C. Ask one of your juniors to talk to the relatives, to let them know that you cannot see them because you are busy, and to deal with any queries.

D. Tell the nurse that you will only grant the relatives 5 minutes and no more as you are busy.

E. Inform your Registrar that you need to see the relatives and ask him whether he can cover for you.

F. Tell the nurse to send the relatives to PALS as your involvement with the patient is over.

G. Tell the nurse to find an excuse to send the relatives home as the patient is dead and the matter is therefore less important than the patients that you are currently dealing with.

Suggested answer and approach
Here are some issues that should cross your mind when reading this scenario:

A – You are using another team member appropriately; the nurse is already with the relatives and it makes sense that you may want to know more about the relatives' request in order to ensure that you can have the relevant information ready when you do meet with them eventually.

B – This may be a little inconvenient for the relatives as they would obviously prefer to get answers straight away. But you are being honest with them and there is a feeling that you want to get their queries resolved even if it is only on the phone.

C – This is potentially placing your junior in a difficult situation and it also looks a little like you are trying to pass the buck. But this is a possibility.

D – This places the nurse in a difficult position. It is also a fairly aggressive stance.

E – Talking to your Registrar may help you identify a good way around the problem. Also, if you need to go and see the relatives, then this option will make the Registrar aware of the situation and the team will be able to deal with your temporary absence.

F – PALS won't be able to deal with the relatives' queries. They will only encourage the relatives to contact you so it will defer the problem. It may sound like a good tactic in the short term but it is really unhelpful. In any case, you should consider it part of your duty to deal with the relatives, particularly if you have been dealing with the patient before his death.

G – This is rude both to the relatives and to the nurse, whom you will place in a difficult position.

There are therefore four possible candidates for the most appropriate actions: A, B, C and E. We need to eliminate one: it will be C because of the potential difficulty to which you will be exposing your junior colleague.

The answer is therefore A, B and E. (Note that these do not need to be ranked.)

13

ISCMEDICAL
Interview Skills Consulting

14

Section 3

Practice questions

SCENARIO 1

You are working on a busy ward, having to deal with many admissions every morning. You share the workload with another junior colleague who has been constantly late by 20 minutes for the past week. What do you do?

Choose the three most appropriate actions to take in this situation:

A. You call your colleague's wife to see whether your colleague has personal problems which may explain his delay.

B. You arrange a discussion with your colleague, express your discontent and tell him to make sure that he comes on time as his delay is slowing you down.

C. You arrange a discussion with your colleague to enquire about the reasons behind the delay.

D. You work harder to compensate for his absence, in the knowledge that his delay is likely to be short term.

E. You discuss your concerns with a group of nurses from your ward to gain insight into his behaviour at work.

F. You mention the delay to your Registrar and ask him whether he can deal with it.

G. In order to avoid confrontation with the colleague you do nothing for the time being, knowing senior colleagues will soon notice his behaviour.

ISCMEDICAL
Interview Skills Consulting

SCENARIO 2

A patient has complained to you that a small amount of cash has disappeared from his bedside table. What do you do?

**Rank each of the following options from 1 to 5
(1= Most appropriate; 5= Least appropriate):**

A. Organise a team meeting and ask the culprit to replace the money as soon as possible.

B. Call the police. Theft is a criminal offence.

C. Ask the patient for details about the alleged theft, reassure him that you will do what you can to deal with the issue, and notify a senior nurse of the problem.

D. Send an email to all your colleagues notifying them of the incident and asking them to warn their patients to be careful about personal possessions.

E. Remind the patient that he should have been more careful about his possessions and tell him that you will see what you can do.

After a long day, the SHO who was meant to take over from you has called in sick 10 minutes before the end of your shift, just as you were supposed to hand over to him. You had arranged to go out with friends that evening and they are expecting you in 2 hours' time. What do you do?

Rank each of the following options from 1 to 5 (1= Most appropriate; 5= Least appropriate):

A. Do your colleague's shift for him. He can then take on one of your shifts when he gets back.

B. Stay for two hours and hand over to the Registrar on call afterwards.

C. Contact the Registrar on call to hand over to him and go home to prepare for your evening.

D. Contact the Registrar on call to hand over to him, offer to stay behind for a couple of hours and join your friends later.

E. Explain to your colleague that this places you in a difficult position, offer to stay for an hour and ask him to come in an hour's time to take over as you cannot stay any longer.

SCENARIO 4

During a ward round, your Consultant prescribes penicillin on a drug chart whose allergy box has been left blank by the admitting doctor. The patient's hospital notes clearly state a penicillin allergy. Having spotted the discrepancy, the nurse brings you the chart a short while later to cross off the penicillin and prescribe an alternative. What would you do subsequently?

Choose the three most appropriate actions to take in this situation:

A. You contact a senior nurse and express concerns at the fact that the allergy was not mentioned on the drug chart.

B. You discuss the incident with your Consultant and complete a critical incident form.

C. You inform the patient that you have correctly identified he is allergic and that you will get back to the Consultant to discuss how the misunderstanding took place.

D. You organise a meeting with your Consultant to discuss the reasons behind his decision to prescribe penicillin when the notes clearly showed that the patient was allergic.

E. You organise a team meeting to discuss the problem and to give the person responsible a chance to explain why the incident happened.

F. You bring the issue up at the next junior doctors' meeting without mentioning the name of the offending doctor.

G. You report the admitting doctor to a senior pharmacist for possible escalation of the matter and retraining.

SCENARIO 5

After a 13-hour day, you are waiting for the arrival of your colleague so that you can hand over to him. You are exhausted because you have just switched over from a week of nights and you are starting to feel sleepy. Your colleague is already 15 minutes late and has not called to say that he is ill. What do you do?

Rank each of the following options from 1 to 5
(1= Most appropriate; 5= Least appropriate):

A. Inform your Registrar that you are too tired to stay and that you need to leave immediately because you cannot function effectively.

B. Go and see your consultant and let him know that, because you are in breach of the 13-hour limit imposed by the European Working Time Directive, you will hand over to him before leaving.

C. Patiently wait for your colleague and cover his shift until he arrives.

D. Hand over to a nurse and leave the hospital.

E. Contact your colleague to see what the matter is and how long the delay is likely to last.

SCENARIO 6

One of your patients, a taxi driver, has recently been diagnosed with epilepsy. Before discharge, you made him aware of his duty to inform the DVLA. You have also made it clear to him that he should not be driving at this current time. On a shopping trip to town, you see him at the wheel picking up a passenger. What do you do?

Rank in order the following actions in response to this situation (1= Most appropriate; 5= Least appropriate):

A. Report the matter to his boss

B. Call the patient to express your concerns and organise a meeting with him to discuss the incident.

C. Call the patient's wife to express your concerns and enlist her help to stop the patient from driving.

D. Report the matter to the DVLA.

E. Send a letter to the patient warning him that you will report him to the DVLA next time you see him pick up a customer.

SCENARIO 7

You have arranged to go out for dinner with your partner tonight. Just before leaving your shift you have been informed that a junior doctors' teaching session that was meant to take place tomorrow morning has now been brought forward and starts in 10 minutes. What do you do?

**Rank each of the following options from 1 to 5
(1= Most appropriate; 5= Least appropriate):**

A. Tell another junior doctor to apologise to the group for your absence.

B. Find out what the meeting is about and discuss with the person running the meeting whether your attendance is strictly necessary as you have organised a dinner with your partner.

C. Slip away unnoticed.

D. Tell a nurse to let the organiser know that you cannot make it.

E. Call your partner and inform him/her that you cannot make the dinner as you must attend an important teaching session.

SCENARIO 8

During a discussion with a fellow junior doctor in the mess, you notice that a bag of marijuana has fallen out of his bag. What do you do?

Choose the three most appropriate <u>immediate</u> actions to take in this situation:

A. Inform the GMC as it is not appropriate for any doctor to take drugs since it can endanger patients.

B. Call the police as marijuana is an illegal substance.

C. Recommend that your colleague considers professional help.

D. Have a discussion with your colleague about the incident to understand what the situation is.

E. Seek his reassurance that he is not using the drug, and tell him that you will keep quiet about the incident if he flushes it down the toilet.

F. Discuss the incident with your Registrar.

G. Report the incident to the Clinical Director.

SCENARIO 9

One of your Consultants came in this morning obviously drunk. You have advised him to go home but he has dismissed you and is about to start his regular clinic. What do you do?

Choose the three most appropriate actions to take in this situation:

A. Call the GMC to warn them of the problem.

B. Discuss cancelling the clinic session with the outpatients administrator / clinic manager.

C. See another Consultant to discuss the situation.

D. Let the Consultant run the clinic and ask him to contact you if at any point he feels unable to continue running the clinic so that someone else can take over.

E. Insist that the Consultant should only see patients with a chaperone.

F. Sit in the clinic with the Consultant yourself to ensure that patients are safe.

G. Complete a critical incident form.

SCENARIO 10

One of your friends, who is asthmatic and works as an engineer, is going on holiday to Europe tomorrow. He has forgotten to order a repeat prescription for his inhaler. He is asking you whether you can help in any way. What do you do?

Rank in order the following actions in response to this situation (1= Most appropriate; 5= Least appropriate):

A. Tell him to go to his nearest A&E.

B. Get an inhaler from A&E yourself.

C. Get an inhaler from the ward.

D. Ask him to contact his GP.

E. Write a prescription for him.

SCENARIO 11

One of your colleagues arrives consistently late for his shifts. What do you do?

Rank each of the following options from 1 to 5
(1= Most appropriate; 5= Least appropriate):

A. Tell their senior about the delays.

B. Discuss the problem with other junior doctors.

C. Approach your late colleague, tell him that his lateness is causing problems and that he must be on time.

D. Ask your colleague if there is a reason for being late and whether there is anything you can do to help.

E. Make a record of the lateness and watch and wait.

SCENARIO 12

A colleague asks you to review one of his patients as he is busy on the ward. This means that you will have to stay late but it is already 5pm and you are about to go out with your family, who have come to collect you. What do you do?

Rank each of the following options from 1 to 5
(1= Most appropriate; 5= Least appropriate):

A. Agree to see the patient and tell your family to go home.

B. See the patient quickly and ask your family to stay in the waiting room.

C. Ask your colleague to hand over the job to the SHO on call.

D. Contact the SHO on call yourself and hand over the job

E. Tell your Consultant to see the patient.

27

SCENARIO 13

You are about to give a case presentation to your department when a nurse bleeps you for an emergency on the ward. What do you do?

**Rank each of the following options from 1 to 5
(1= Most appropriate; 5= Least appropriate):**

A. Go straight away without telling anybody.

B. Tell the nurse that you cannot attend the patient but that you will go after the meeting.

C. Ask a colleague to attend the ward.

D. Cancel the teaching session and attend the emergency.

E. Apologise to the team at the meeting and ask a colleague to fill in while you find out more information and see if you need to attend at once.

28

SCENARIO 14

One of your colleagues confides in you that he has a cocaine addiction problem. He is asking you to keep the information to yourself as he needs your support and no aggravation. What do you do?

Rank each of the following options from 1 to 5
(1= Most appropriate; 5= Least appropriate):

A. Tell your colleague that you have no option but to report the matter to a senior straight away.

B. Reassure your colleague that you will support him but tell him that he needs to address the matter with his seniors, otherwise you will have no option but to tell them yourself.

C. Report the matter to a Consultant without telling your colleague that you have done so.

D. Agree with your colleague and keep quiet about it.

E. Investigate whether your colleague has performance problems and report the matter to the Consultant if he has any.

29

SCENARIO 15

A patient has revealed to you that they have a history of taking illegal substances. They are begging you to delete any mention of drug-taking from the notes as it could compromise their medical insurance if the information ever came to light. What do you do?

Choose the three most appropriate actions to take in this situation:

A. Reassure the patient that you are bound by a duty of confidentiality and you simply cannot divulge any information about them to a third party without their consent.

B. Tell the patient that you cannot guarantee his confidentiality but that you will inform him first if you need to breach it.

C. Tell the patient that you simply cannot delete any information from the notes.

D. Delete the information from the notes.

E. Delete the information from the notes if it has no relevance to the patient's current health problems.

F. Tell the patient that you will have to reveal the information if asked by the insurance company.

G. Contact the insurance company naming the patient, inform them of the issue and ask for advice.

SCENARIO 16

A young patient, whom you have been treating on your ward for the first time, offers you a £100 book voucher to thank you for your help in their recovery on your ward. During their short admission your only contact with the patient was with the team during ward rounds. You do not expect the patient to come back for another stay on your ward. What do you do?

Rank each of the following options from 1 to 5
(1= Most appropriate; 5= Least appropriate):

A. Tell the patient that you cannot accept the gift because it would not be ethical.

B. Accept the gift and give it to your wife/husband/partner.

C. Accept the gift and put it towards ward funds.

D. Politely refuse the gift because their recovery is the best recompense for you.

E. Accept the gift but tell the patient not to let any of the team know as you do not want any trouble.

SCENARIO 17

You are dealing with a ward patient whose wife's best friend works on your ward as a nurse. The patient has asked you specifically to ensure that no information about his health should be given to the nurse in question so that his wife cannot gain information about his health. What do you do?

Rank each of the following options from 1 to 5
(1= Most appropriate; 5= Least appropriate):

A. Inform the patient that there is nothing that you can do about it and that they will need to put up with the situation as it stands.

B. Have a word with the rest of the team to ensure that the patient's confidentiality is maintained.

C. Tell the nurse that she must take some time off whilst the patient is in the ward so as not to compromise his right to confidentiality.

D. Have a word with the patient to understand the reasons behind his request and see if there is a possible compromise that can be reached.

E. Transfer the patient to another part of the ward where the nurse does not work.

Interview Skills Consulting

SCENARIO 18

During a clinic run by your Consultant, you walk into the room and find the Consultant with his arms around the patient's shoulder. What do you do?

Rank each of the following options from 1 to 5
(1= Most appropriate; 5= Least appropriate):

A. Assume that there must be a reasonable explanation for the situation and ignore the issue.

B. Ask the patient to leave the room so that you can have a word with the Consultant.

C. Report the matter to the Clinical Director.

D. Have a word with the Consultant after the patient has left and ask him about the circumstances.

E. Seek advice from the Registrar who is running the clinic next door.

ℬ

⨉

∠⟩

𝒦

𝒟ᵢ

33

SCENARIO 19

During a late-running clinic, one of your colleagues is reduced to tears after receiving racist remarks from one of the patients in anger at the delay he is experiencing. Your colleague is distressed and has told you that she does not want to see that patient. What do you do?

Rank each of the following options from 1 to 5
(1= Most appropriate; 5= Least appropriate):

A. Tell the patient to go home and to book another appointment with another doctor once he has calmed down.

B. Agree to see the patient and explain to the patient at the start of the consultation that what he did was unacceptable.

C. Tell the patient that he will be seen but by a different doctor and that he will need to wait until one of them is free. If he does not like this, he has the opportunity to rebook another appointment.

D. See him yourself and make sure that his appointments are scheduled early on the list in future.

E. Tell your colleague to see the patient, as she should learn to handle such situations by herself.

"ISCMEDICAL
Interview Skills Consulting

SCENARIO 20

You work in a GP practice and you require an ECG urgently for a patient who is experiencing chest pains. There is one ECG machine in the practice but it is new and you simply have not had time to learn how to use it. Only one of the nurses knows how to operate the machine and she appears to be busy with a patient at present. What do you do?

Rank each of the following options from 1 to 5
(1= Most appropriate; 5= Least appropriate):

A. Search for the instructions in the supply cupboard.

B. Interrupt the nurse and ask if she is able to carry out the ECG straight away.

C. Using your experience of previous models, perform the ECG yourself.

D. Call an ambulance and send the patient to A&E.

E. Send the patient home and ask him to call you if the pain gets worse.

Interview Skills Consulting

SCENARIO 21

You work in a GP practice and you require an ECG urgently for a patient. There is one ECG machine in the practice but it is new and you simply have not had time to learn how to use it. Only one of the nurses knows how to operate the machine. When you asked the nurse to carry out the ECG, she replied in an angry tone that she was too busy when, in reality, she was simply doing some filing. With no other alternative, you sent the patient to A&E. What do you do next?

Choose the three most appropriate actions to take in this situation:

A. Inform the nurse that she compromised the safety of the patient, ask for an explanation and explain that you will need to inform the head of the practice next time such an incident takes place.

B. Bring this up at the next management meeting to see if anyone else has experienced that problem and whether any personnel matters should be attended to.

C. Organise for training for yourself and the rest of the team on the ECG machine.

D. Organise a discussion with the nurse to understand the basis of her behaviour.

E. Report the incident to the head of the PCT.

F. Write to the patient informing him that he can make a complaint if he wants to.

G. Send an email to all your colleagues asking them to watch out for that nurse as she may cause problems.

SCENARIO 22

A 25-year-old pregnant Indian woman who cannot speak English presents to your GP surgery accompanied by her father. The father tells you that his daughter would like to have a termination of pregnancy. What do you do?

Rank each of the following options from 1 to 5
(1= Most appropriate; 5= Least appropriate):

A. Ask the father to interpret for his daughter.

B. Obtain an interpreter and discuss the situation with the patient and her father.

C. Obtain an interpreter and ask the father to leave the room so that you can talk to the patient alone.

D. Ask the father if someone else from the family could interpret for the daughter.

E. Attempt to talk to the daughter through the use of diagrams and other non-verbal means.

37

SCENARIO 23

Mrs Smith is a 70-year-old lady who has been your patient for over 30 years and whom you see regularly throughout the year. She gives you a standard bottle of your favourite drink for your birthday. What do you do?

**Rank each of the following options from 1 to 5
(1= Most appropriate; 5= Least appropriate):**

A. Refuse the gift because it is against regulations.

B. Graciously accept the gift, telling the patient that it is kind of her.

C. Accept the gift but make sure that the practice manager is aware of it.

D. Accept the gift but tell the patient that it has to be the last time.

E. Refuse the gift but double-check with your defence union afterwards.

SCENARIO 24

In a clinic, a female patient mentions that, during her previous consultation, one of your colleagues examined her breasts. This seems odd to you as there is nothing mentioned in the notes. What do you do?

**Rank each of the following options from 1 to 5
(1= Most appropriate; 5= Least appropriate):**

A. Ask the patient about the circumstances surrounding the examination and, after the consultation, ask your colleague for further details on the issue.

B. Tell the patient that this might constitute an assault and explain the complaint procedure to her.

C. Say nothing to the patient and report the incident to the Clinical Director.

D. Seek advice from a trusted senior colleague.

E. Contact the GMC.

SCENARIO 25

Another junior doctor on your team confides in you that he has contracted Hepatitis C during his previous job and needs your advice. He would appreciate that you keep the matter confidential. What do you do?

Choose the three most appropriate actions to take in this situation:

A. Inform the Personnel/Medical Staffing department.

B. Refer your colleague to Occupational Health to be vaccinated.

C. Discuss the matter with a senior colleague.

D. Discuss the situation with a senior colleague if you see that your colleague performs risky procedures.

E. Ask a senior sister to alert you if he is doing any exposure-prone procedure.

F. Recommend to your colleague that he should get advice from his defence union.

G. Recommend to your colleague that he should discuss the matter with his seniors.

SCENARIO 26

You have noticed that one of the Consultants on your team is often making remarks of a sexual nature to one of the secretaries. On the surface she does not seem to be affected by this. What do you do?

Choose the three most appropriate actions to take in this situation:

A. Encourage the secretary to check the staff manual to determine what action she should take.

B. Let the secretary know that you have observed the Consultant harass her and that she should raise the issue with her seniors.

C. Arrange a discussion with the Consultant in question to let him know that such behaviour must stop.

D. Approach a senior colleague that you can trust to discuss the matter.

E. Contact the GMC, who will handle the situation from then on.

F. Inform the HR or personnel department.

G. Wait until the next incident to mention something to the Consultant about how inappropriate his remark was.

SCENARIO 27

In the past few minutes, you have flushed an intravenous cannula with lidocaine instead of saline. The patient does not seem to be experiencing any adverse reaction. What do you do?

Choose the three most appropriate actions to take in this situation:

A. Tell the patient that you have made a mistake, apologise and offer the means to make a complaint if he so wishes.

B. Bleep your Registrar for information and further advice.

C. Wait 5 more minutes and if the patient is fine then do not take any further action.

D. Write the mistake in the notes but do not notify the patient as there was no adverse reaction.

E. Tell the patient that you have injected a bit of local anaesthetic (which is a procedure that is sometimes carried out) so as to be open but not to worry him.

F. Explain to the patient that you have made a mistake caused by wrong labelling, which is the nurse's responsibility. Give the patient the means to make a complaint against the nurse if he so wishes.

G. Complete a critical incident form.

SCENARIO 28

Your Registrar looks permanently tired. You know that he has been working very hard over the past few months. He seems to be burning himself out and makes simple mistakes every day, though none have actually had any adverse effect on patients so far. What do you do?

Choose the three most appropriate actions to take in this situation:

A. Approach the Registrar and express your concerns about his health and the simple mistakes that he has been making.

B. Inform the Registrar that all mistakes, even small, are a danger to patients and that you will have no choice but to talk to the Consultant if the situation does not improve.

C. Discuss with your Registrar the possibility to take on some of his work.

D. Encourage the Registrar to raise the issue with his Consultant to find a workable solution to the situation.

E. Contact Medical Staffing to see if they can get a locum to relieve the pressure on the Registrar.

F. Inform Occupational Health and encourage them to contact the Registrar before it is too late.

G. Complete a critical incident form the next time a mistake occurs.

SCENARIO 29

You are a GP and you are seeing a newly registered patient, a 30-year-old heroin addict who is asking for methadone. The patient's notes have not arrived from his previous practice. What do you do?

Rank each of the following options from 1 to 5
(1= Most appropriate; 5= Least appropriate):

A. Ask the patient which dose he normally takes and prescribe one dose only.

B. Send the patient to A&E.

C. Tell the patient that you cannot prescribe any controlled drugs until his notes have arrived.

D. Call his previous GP, check the normal dose previously prescribed and prescribe one dose to the patient.

E. Prescribe the patient one week's worth of an average dose of methadone and call his GP to ensure that his notes reach you within one week.

SCENARIO 30

One Friday morning, one of your colleagues calls the ward from his home and says that he will not be coming in as he is feeling unwell. Subsequently, you find out that in fact he spent a long weekend abroad with his family and was never ill in the first place. What do you do?

**Rank each of the following options from 1 to 5
(1= Most appropriate; 5= Least appropriate):**

A. Do nothing.

B. Tell your Consultant as soon as you find out about the lie.

C. Ask the colleague in question about the situation and warn him that you will have no option but to mention something to the Consultant if this reoccurs.

D. Discuss the matter with your fellow junior doctors.

E. Ask the colleague about the situation at the next team meeting.

SCENARIO 31

You walk into the doctors' mess and see one of your Registrars watching child pornography on his laptop. What do you do?

Rank each of the following options from 1 to 5
(1= Most appropriate; 5= Least appropriate):

A. Nothing. He is watching the images on his private computer and therefore it is his own business.

B. Call the police. Child pornography is illegal.

C. Send an anonymous note to your colleague saying that you spotted him watching the images and that the Consultant will be warned next time it happens.

D. Approach a senior colleague that you can trust and let them handle the matter.

E. Notify the HR department.

SCENARIO 32

You walk into the doctors' mess and see one of your Registrars watching standard adult pornography on a hospital computer. What do you do?

Choose the three most appropriate actions to take in this situation:

A. Notify Personnel as this is clearly an abuse of NHS property.

B. Tell your colleague that it is not really appropriate to watch these kinds of images on hospital property and that he should be careful as some people may find it offensive.

C. Discuss the situation with other junior colleagues and confront him as a group so as to have maximum impact and make him stop.

D. Have a word with your Consultant if this occurs too often.

E. Have a word with your Consultant if the Registrar's performance is affected by his activities.

F. Contact the IT department so that they can monitor the computer's activities.

G. Notify the police.

SCENARIO 33

One of the nurses you used to work with on another ward tells you that one her colleagues was very drunk during the Christmas party and was heavily flirting with one of the paramedics. Her seniors were not present at the party. What do you do?

**Rank each of the following options from 1 to 5
(1= Most appropriate; 5= Least appropriate):**

A. Do nothing.

B. Approach the nurse and tell her that by making a fool of herself, she acted unprofessionally.

C. Have a word with one of her seniors.

D. Ask your Consultant to have a word with one of her seniors.

E. Contact the Director of Nursing about the issue.

SCENARIO 34

You see a nurse pick antibiotics out of a drug trolley and place them in her handbag for personal use. What do you do?

**Rank each of the following options from 1 to 5
(1= Most appropriate; 5= Least appropriate):**

A. Approach the nurse in question and explain that it is not best practice.

B. Report the matter to your Consultant.

C. Report the matter to a senior nurse.

D. Report the matter to the Director of Nursing.

E. Write a critical incident form.

SCENARIO 35

You work with only one other junior colleague on the ward. It is 3pm and all ward jobs have been completed. The shift normally ends at 5pm but your colleague says that he is going out for a birthday meal and would like to leave straight away so that he has time to go home, get ready and drive to the restaurant. What do you do?

Choose the three most appropriate actions to take in this situation:

A. Make sure that he has agreed it with the Registrar before he leaves.

B. Let him slip away without a word so that no fuss is made.

C. Take his bleep from him.

D. Insist that he stays.

E. Tell him to clear it with Medical Staffing.

F. Make him double-check that there is nothing left to be done before he leaves.

G. Ask him to redirect his bleep to the doctor on call for the evening.

SCENARIO 36

You leave the hospital and see a tramp on a bus stop bench just outside A&E. He is holding an empty bottle of wine and is vomiting on the pavement. What do you do?

Rank each of the following options from 1 to 5
(1= Most appropriate; 5= Least appropriate):

A. Walk past him and ignore him.

B. Go up to the tramp and see if he is okay.

C. Take him to A&E.

D. Go to A&E yourself and ask a member of the team to take charge of the tramp.

E. Call 999.

SCENARIO 37

During a ward round with your Consultant (your Registrar is away today), a patient goes into cardiac arrest. The arrest call has been put out and the team has yet to arrive. Having completed your ALS course a month ago and led several arrests since, you are best placed to assume the role of team leader. Your Consultant has not recertified his ALS for many years but is now giving orders that you know are inappropriate. What do you do?

Rank each of the following options from 1 to 5
(1= Most appropriate; 5= Least appropriate):

A. Ensure that only basic life support is being given while you are waiting for the arrest team to arrive.

B. Let the Consultant take over the handling of the arrest and discuss with him later how it may be better to let colleagues more experienced with cardiac arrest lead such situations in future.

C. Let the Consultant give orders but signal to the nurses to do differently when you feel his orders are not appropriate.

D. Reassure the Consultant that you are the most experienced and up-to-date person on the team. Then take over the leadership of the team.

E. Ask a nurse to call another Consultant with cardiac arrest experience from the adjacent ward. Let your Consultant lead the arrest while waiting for the other Consultant to arrive.

SCENARIO 38

During a bedside teaching session, your Consultant asks you a range of questions, some of which you struggle to answer. Towards the end of the session, you are left with the feeling that the Consultant is rude and has embarrassed you in front of the patient. What do you do?

Choose the three most appropriate actions to take in this situation:

A. Contact the Human Resources department to complain about the incident.

B. Complain about the incident to a senior nurse.

C. Take some time out to think about the incident and how you might want to react to it.

D. Argue with the Consultant at the bedside so that he knows straight away that he is being harsh on you.

E. Once the session is over, apologise to the patient about the Consultant's behaviour.

F. Arrange a meeting with the Consultant to discuss the incident.

G. Complete a critical incident form.

H. Discuss the incident with your educational supervisor.

SCENARIO 39

You walk into the mess and find one of your colleagues taking a sip at a bottle of whisky, whilst you know that his shift does not end for another 3 hours. What do you do?

**Rank each of the following options from 1 to 5
(1= Most appropriate; 5= Least appropriate):**

A. Let your colleague know that his behaviour makes him unsafe towards patients and that, as a result, you will need to inform his educational supervisor.

B. As your colleague does not appear drunk, let the matter drop without addressing the issue with him in case he becomes embarrassed.

C. As your colleague does not appear drunk, let the matter drop but let him know that you will need to talk to senior colleagues if you catch him again.

D. Discuss the situation with your colleague to determine the reasons for his drinking and offer to help him out. Encourage your colleague to discuss the situation with his seniors.

E. At the end of your colleague's shift, organise a meeting with other junior doctors to discuss how you can best proceed.

SCENARIO 40

You are bleeped to attend a crash call for Mr Smith who is arresting. On reading the notes, you do not find any DNR order and proceed with CPR, unsuccessfully. A little while later, whilst reading another patient's notes, you notice a DNR order for Mr Smith, which had evidently been misfiled. The relatives have witnessed the arrest. They are upset and are still with the patient. What do you do?

Choose the three most appropriate actions to take in this situation:

A. Contact your Consultant and complete a critical incident form.

B. Contact your Consultant but complete a critical incident form only later on when/if such misfiling happens again.

C. Let the resuscitation team know about the recently discovered DNR form.

D. Nothing, since the patient has died.

E. Talk to the relatives in a separate room.

F. Wait until your Consultant comes back to talk to the relatives.

G. Inform senior managers at Trust level.

SCENARIO 41

A 17-year-old female patient presents to your surgery covered with severe bruises. She explains that she lives with a criminal who sometimes beats her up when he is high on drugs. When you offer to help her out, she refuses to allow you to tell anyone about it.

**Rank each of the following options from 1 to 5
(1= Most appropriate; 5= Least appropriate):**

A. Maintain your patient's confidentiality and do nothing.

B. Tell the patient that, unless she cooperates, you will have no alternative but to contact social services or the police.

C. Seek advice from one of your senior colleagues about how you should proceed.

D. Ask the girl if she would be prepared to discuss the issue with someone from social services. If she refuses, do it anyway but without her knowledge.

E. Contact her partner to discuss the situation with him.

SCENARIO 42

During your on calls you work with a Registrar who is often unobtainable. For the fifth time in a week, you bleeped him to review a very sick patient urgently and he has failed to turn up. Whenever you ask him where he has been, his only excuse is that his bleep functions erratically and that he wasn't aware that you had bleeped him. What do you do?

Choose the three most appropriate actions to take in this situation:

A. Contact your Consultant to inform him about the problem.

B. Ignore the problem but make sure that whenever you require help on a patient-related matter you seek advice from another suitable Registrar.

C. Ignore the problem but make sure that whenever you require help on a patient-related matter you seek advice from another junior doctor at your level.

D. Initiate a meeting with your Registrar to get to the bottom of the problem.

E. Ask some of the nurses whether they have heard the Registrar's bleep go off so as to check whether he is telling the truth.

F. Complete a critical incident form.

G. Complain to a senior nurse about the problem.

SCENARIO 43

A patient presents to A&E. He is very impatient and insists on the best possible care. You diagnose folliculitis and recommend salt water bathing and a no-shave period. The patient does not want to take your advice and demands to be referred to a dermatologist for a second opinion. What do you do?

Rank each of the following options from 1 to 5
(1= Most appropriate; 5= Least appropriate):

A. Tell the patient that he will need to go back to his GP in order to be referred to a dermatologist.

B. Reassure the patient that you are confident about the diagnosis and that he should trust you.

C. Ask another doctor from A&E to review the patient to confirm the diagnosis as a second opinion.

D. Tell the patient that you can refer him privately if he wants a referral to a dermatologist.

E. Ask the patient to come back on another day to see a different A&E doctor.

SCENARIO 44

Your hospital has recently been in the news because of an adverse event and a phone call from a journalist is being transferred to you in the very busy A&E department where you work. What do you do?

**Rank each of the following options from 1 to 5
(1= Most appropriate; 5= Least appropriate):**

A. Tell the journalist that you are confident that the hospital is doing a very good job and that you know that everything is being done to remedy difficult situations quickly and efficiently.

B. Tell the journalist that you cannot speak with him and put the phone down.

C. Tell the journalist that, if he gives you his contact details, you will pass them on to the relevant person.

D. Tell the journalist to contact the Trust's Press Officer.

E. Tell the journalist that you will call them back at the end of your shift when you have more time to speak.

SCENARIO 45

You are doing an audit for your practice. It is Friday lunchtime and you must present your preliminary results on Monday morning to your supervisor. To finish the current phase of the audit you still need to enter data from the notes of 20 patients into a database that resides on your own laptop. In view of your workload, you may not be able to collect all the remaining data before the end of the day. The practice will be closed during the weekend and you do not have the keys. What do you do?

Rank each of the following options from 1 to 5
(1= Most appropriate; 5= Least appropriate):

A.   Take the patients' notes home with you to continue the data input at home over the weekend.

B.   Make photocopies of the relevant pages of the patient notes, removing any patient-identifiable information, and take these photocopies back home with you to work on over the weekend.

C.   Draw a quick plan of the data required on a piece of paper and quickly collect the data needed before the practice shuts for the day.

D.   Look at the average profile of the patients that you have already entered into your database and create new patient data matching the average profile in order to reach the number of patients discussed with your supervisor.

E.   Ask your supervisor to defer the meeting to another day, once you have had time to complete your input.

SCENARIO 46

One of the nurses on your ward is complaining about the bad body odour of one of your colleagues and is asking you if you could have a word with him. What do you do?

Choose the three most appropriate actions to take in this situation:

A. Tell the nurse that this is really an issue for the Consultant to deal with and that she should go and talk to him.

B. Go and talk to the Consultant about it yourself.

C. Ask a few other colleagues whether they agree with the nurse's view before going to see the Consultant yourself.

D. Raise the issue at a team meeting when the colleague in question is present.

E. Raise the issue at a team meeting in the absence of the colleague in question.

F. Raise the issue in confidence with the colleague in question.

G. Send the colleague an anonymous note asking him to sort the issue out.

SCENARIO 47

You overhear a receptionist talking to one of the regular patients in front of other patients. She is making fun of an ugly patient who came in earlier. What do you do?

**Rank each of the following options from 1 to 5
(1= Most appropriate; 5= Least appropriate):**

A. Firmly tell the receptionist to stop the discussion there and then.

B. Do nothing for the time being but raise the problem with the clinic manager at the next occurrence.

C. Contact the clinic manager immediately, alerting them to the situation.

D. Have a private word with the receptionist once the patient has left.

E. Apologise to the other patients present and reassure them that it will not happen again.

SCENARIO 48

You have written a case report for publication and your Consultant has recently reviewed your final draft. When he gives you his comments back, you notice that he has added two names to the list of authors. On enquiring, he tells you that they are his wife and his ex-Registrar who are both currently unemployed and need publications on their CV to enhance their chances of employment. Neither were involved with the case discussed in your paper. What do you do?

Choose the three most appropriate actions to take in this situation:

A. Tell the Consultant that you cannot publish the case reports with their names on and that you will submit it with your name only.

B. Discuss the situation in confidence with the Clinical Director and envisage contacting the GMC about the two other doctors.

C. Agree to add the two names to the publication as it is only a case report and not a research paper.

D. Check with other colleagues whether something similar has happened to them and contact the GMC about your Consultant if it has.

E. Discuss the matter with the Consultant in a private meeting.

F. Report your Consultant to the GMC.

G. Contact the paper where the case report is due to be published to tell them about the situation.

SCENARIO 49

Your Consultant asks you to make a backdated alteration to the notes in order to cover up for a past mistake made by the team. What do you do?

Choose the three most appropriate actions to take in this situation:

A. Make the change requested by the Consultant as you are worried that he may give you a bad reference.

B. Refuse to make the entry.

C. Make a note of the conversation that you have had with the Consultant and contact your defence union.

D. Report the matter to the Clinical Director at the earliest opportunity.

E. Inform the patient of the Consultant's request and of the mistake made.

F. Inform the GMC.

G. Inform the police as there are potentially legal implications.

SCENARIO 50

You work as the SHO on a general surgical ward. A 20-year-old girl was brought in earlier to A&E by her father after collapsing in the street. She subsequently developed abdominal pains and has been accepted by your team. She is now clinically stable and preliminary tests are unremarkable. Her father is on the phone to you, asking for information about his daughter's admission. What do you do?

Rank each of the following options from 1 to 5
(1= Most appropriate; 5= Least appropriate):

A. Tell the father that you simply cannot communicate with him on any matter relating to his daughter as this would be breaching her confidentiality.

B. Reassure the father that his daughter is fine but that you cannot give any further details without talking to his daughter first.

C. Explain to the father that his daughter has developed abdominal pains but that you cannot give any further details without talking to his daughter first.

D. Explain to the father that you will need to determine whether his daughter is competent before deciding whether you are able to release any further details to him.

E. Hand the phone over to the Registrar and ask him to handle the call.

SCENARIO 51

A woman presents to your surgery and explains that she has caught a sexually-transmitted infection (STI). The infection must have come from her husband since she is "faithful". The patient thinks that her husband came to see you recently and she suspects that it was about an STI. In fact, he came to see you last week telling you that he was "100% faithful" and thought that he might have caught an infection from his wife. What do you do?

Rank each of the following options from 1 to 5
(1= Most appropriate; 5= Least appropriate):

A. Tell her that you got a completely different story from her husband as he felt that he had caught his infection from her.

B. Seek advice from a colleague about how to handle the matter.

C. Tell her that the husband indeed came to see you but that you are not at liberty to divulge the matters discussed during the consultation.

D. Tell her that you cannot discuss any issues relating to other patients, including whether or not they have attended your surgery recently.

E. Tell her that you are facing a potential conflict of interest and that she should register with another GP.

SCENARIO 52

You have been charged with providing a series of lectures to final year medical students on a range of topics with which you are very familiar. One of the students whom you know well has somehow managed to get hold of a photocopy of the forthcoming exam papers and asks you to make sure that you address all the relevant issues at your teaching sessions. What do you do?

**Rank each of the following options from 1 to 5
(1= Most appropriate; 5= Least appropriate):**

A. Confiscate the papers and report the matter straight away to the deanery, naming the student involved.

B. Confiscate the papers and report the matter straight away to the deanery, withholding the student's name.

C. Advise him to throw away the papers without looking at them.

D. Ignore the matter.

E. Inform the student that in order to maintain a fair process he will need to make sure that all other students also have a copy of the exam papers.

Section 4

Suggested answers

SCENARIO 1

ANSWER: C, D, F

1. There are two options that can be discounted from the outset:

   ▪ G: doing nothing is never an option unless it is really none of your business (we will see situations like these later) or unless the other options are obviously worse than doing nothing (e.g. unsafe). In this particular option, you are prompted to do nothing because you think someone else will notice the issue. This means that you prefer to keep quiet, hoping that it will become someone else's problem. Imagine the consequences if your colleague's lateness contributed one day to the death of a patient. In a situation where patient care is potentially affected by the delay, you simply cannot afford to ignore the matter

   ▪ E: If there is a problem to discuss, you should discuss first with other junior colleagues or a senior colleague but not with the nurses. This will only spread gossip and create a bad atmosphere.

2. Notice that B and C both talk about arranging a discussion with the colleague but differ on how the discussion should be approached.

   ▪ B is more like a dressing-down ("express your discontent"), which could potentially result in conflict.

   ▪ C, however, is softer, more appropriate for the occasion and hints that you keep an open mind about the reasons behind the delay. Indeed, your colleague is likely to have a good reason to be late. It could be something as common-place as train problems, or a sick child or a more serious issue such as depression. Getting your facts right and taking a sensitive approach will help you identify the best way forward.

   C is the more acceptable option of the two as it is taking a softer approach to a problem which is not yet a major issue. Although forceful, D may be acceptable too, but only if there is no better option that we can identify.

3. This leaves us with A, C, D and F. As we have seen, C is appropriate as it helps establish the situation in a soft manner. D is also appropriate because, if your colleague is not performing in line with expectations, you must make sure the patient is adequately covered at all times, even if this means working harder temporarily.

4. The final choice between A (calling his wife) and F (mentioning to the Registrar) goes in favour of F because (i) if he has personal problems, the last thing you want to do is make it worse by telling his wife (it is not your place to interfere with his private life) and (ii) involving the Registrar is the safest option, particularly if the problem is likely to last. The Registrar will then address the problem with the colleague, which is likely to yield better results than to involve your colleague's wife.

5. This leaves us with C, D and F.

Important note
When you attempt to answer questions in this "pick three out of seven" format, you would normally start by separating the options that appear reasonable from those which are not reasonable. However, a clever question may contain a list of options which are all reasonable or all unreasonable. Your task is to find those which are the best or the "least bad" in the list. For that reason, no option can be totally excluded unless you have identified three better other options. In this particular question, B was discounted because it felt a bit forceful. But, for example, if F had been "You report your colleague to the Clinical Director" instead of "You mention the delay to the Registrar" then the answer would have been B, C and D; in other words, it would have been more appropriate to be a bit forceful with your colleague than to report him straight to the top.

71

SCENARIO 2

ANSWER: 1:C – 2:E – 3:D – 4:A – 5:B

In many cases you will find it easier to determine the level of appropriateness in reverse order (i.e. least appropriate first), as demonstrated here:

1. B (calling the police) has to be the least appropriate. We are only talking about a small amount of cash here. The culprit could be anyone ranging from a patient, a visitor, a nurse, a doctor etc. The police will not be able to do anything about it and you will have achieved nothing by calling them. If the thefts were of controlled drugs, or if the thefts were a regular occurrence, then there would be a stronger case for doing so. However, you would need to discuss with the Clinical Director and head nurse first (i.e. someone in charge would call the police, not you. Otherwise you will alienate the whole team at the hospital).

2. C, D and E all talk about reassuring patients or warning them to be more careful. They therefore look like stronger candidates for appropriateness as they are more in line with common sense. Option A looks good at first glance but it makes the assumption that the culprit is a member of the team. This will create conflict. Do you sincerely think that the culprit will replace the money? Therefore A can be placed as the fourth least effective option.

3. Out of C, D and E, two of the options involve reassuring the victim himself (C and E). D only talks about sending an email to your colleagues to warn patients. This may well be appropriate but your first concern should be with the victim and not the potential future theft of the other patients (this comes later). Therefore, out of the three options, D is the least appropriate.

4. Out of C and E, C is a softer and more caring approach. E is slightly patronising on the patient (he probably already knows he should have been more careful) but still within acceptable limits. In this context, a softer, reassuring approach is required and C is therefore better than E.

SCENARIO 3

ANSWER: 1:D – 2:C – 3:B – 4:A – 5:E

1. E makes no practical sense. If the colleague is sick (and we must take his word for it at this stage), then it would make no sense to expect him to come in an hour later. This has to be the least appropriate option.

2. A is unsafe. You simply cannot expect to do a double shift and remain safe, at least not in comparison to the other options on offer. This has to be the second least appropriate option. Also if someone is sick, then they are officially on sick leave. They should not be expected to make up for it later on.

3. B, C and D all involve contacting the Registrar on call but at different times:
   - B = you stay 2 hours and then involve him
   - C = you involve him and leave
   - D = you involve him, offer to stay for a while and then leave.

   If an SHO is ill, the Registrar will need to know at the first opportunity so that he can manage the situation appropriately. In addition, you should not take additional responsibilities without informing a senior colleague. Therefore, involving him early is best. This places B in third position.

   Between C and D, option D is best because you show solidarity and willingness to help. The Registrar might accept or refuse your offer to stay but that is down to him. In any case, he is also on call and therefore it will be down to him to cover for the SHO. There is no harm in showing a bit of team spirit on your part though.

SCENARIO 4

ANSWER: B, C, F

1. A is inappropriate because it is not a nurse's responsibility to ensure that the drug chart is accurate. Contacting the senior nurse will therefore achieve little.

2. D is inappropriate because the approach is quite confrontational ("organise a meeting"). It makes it look like the Consultant is fully responsible for the mistake and it will not resolve the fundamental question, which is to know why the allergy was not written on the drug chart in the first place. Having said that, it would be true to say that the Consultant should have asked for clarification about the blank allergy box and there may be value in having a word with him about the incident (hence why B is more appropriate).

3. E feels like a tribunal. If someone has made a mistake then the best approach is to go and talk to them so that they can learn from the incident. There is no need for public humiliation. In any case, the admitting doctor might not be part of your own team!

4. G is inappropriate because it is not really the pharmacist's responsibility to train doctors on how to complete drug charts or to take disciplinary action. If the error was a simple one, such action is a bit over the top. It may be a better idea to get the pharmacist to organise a training session on common drug chart errors.

5. This leaves us with B, C and F, all three of which are the most appropriate.

   - C is appropriate because, if the decision was made to give him the penicillin during a ward round, then he might have heard the comment and he needs to be reassured that everything is in hand.

- B is appropriate because it is recognising that a mistake has been made and steps are being taken to discuss the nature of the mistake in a non-confrontational manner (as opposed to option D). Mentioning critical incident reporting highlights your awareness of the importance of clinical risk management and therefore makes this a particularly good option. Some may argue that completing a critical incident form might be over the top but the fact remains that the penicillin was actually written up on the drug chart by the Consultant. A lack of checks further down the line could have had potentially devastating consequences.

- F is appropriate because the team benefits from your experience and you are helping to prevent future occurrences of the same type of mistake. Mentioning the name of the doctor would have little value at this stage since it is the general issue of checking that the box has been completed that really matters as far as the team is concerned.

SCENARIO 5

ANSWER: 1:E – 2:A – 3:B – 4:C – 5:D

1. At first glance, the following observations come to mind:

   - Quoting the EWTD as an excuse to leave (option B) seems a bit over the top, especially to a Consultant. It creates a big drama when there is no need to do so. Why not simply argue patient safety since the question clearly states that you are sleepy?

   - Patiently waiting and covering (option C) when you are exhausted could be unsafe. You have already been waiting for 15 minutes. The wait could be long!

   - Handing over to a nurse could be disastrous. This may lead to miscommunication and errors, and you are assuming that she will know what to do with the information.

   - Your colleague may have been delayed for a good reason and there may not be long for you to wait. The sensible thing to do is therefore to find out more about the situation before you can take any action. Option E therefore seems the obvious starting point. Even if you are tired, it won't take long. If you can't get hold of him or if your colleague is substantially delayed then move to the next stage.

2. Both C and D are unsafe: C is unsafe because you are tired and D is unsafe because the information may never get to the doctor or may be miscommunicated. Also, it is unfair on the nurse (and it is against team spirit) to place the responsibility onto her and it is also bad practice to simply disappear without notifying your colleagues (and in particular your Registrar); therefore, D must be worse than C. Note that both D and C are bad options, but we are simply saying that D is the worst because it compounds several issues (patient safety and bad teamwork).

3. We have now established that E should come first and that C and D should come last. This leaves us with A and B to place in second and third positions. It makes no sense to hand over to your Consultant if the Registrar is available (and nothing in the question states that he is not available). This places A ahead of B. The fact that you used the EWTD as an excuse for handing over to your Consultant also confirms that A goes ahead of B. Quoting regulations may be the right thing to do, but it does not give the impression that you are helping the team to deal with a difficult problem. Regardless of the excuse given, it is the grade that will dictate the answer here, i.e. Registrar first, then Consultant.

Important note:
As mentioned in the introduction, the marking scheme allows for partial marks to be awarded to answers which, although they do not match the "ideal" answer, are also acceptable. In this scenario, answering EBACD instead of EABCD would most likely grant you partial marks.

SCENARIO 6

ANSWER: 1:B – 2:C – 3:D – 4:E – 5:A

1. Option A (reporting the matter to his boss) will achieve little. The boss might be reluctant to lose an employee. At worst, all he can do is sack the employee but that will not resolve the problem, which is that the patient is still driving. It is the worst option.

2. Option D (reporting the matter to the DVLA) may be what you have to do in the end but there are steps that you can take before you take such an official stance. The DVLA guidelines actually say that you must do everything you can to resolve the matter before you contact them (which may include discussing the matter with a next of kin). So that means B and C will have to come before D.

3. The best option is to address the matter with the patient himself. However, this must be done in a manner that invites the patient to comply and therefore must be non-threatening (hence why B is the best).

4. Option E (sending a threatening letter) is a difficult one. On one hand it seems a logical thing to do before you actually report the patient to the DVLA (to warn him of the consequences of his actions), but on the other hand the wording says that you will have to catch him driving before you can report him. This will mean spying on him or relying on luck and it is highly impractical. Therefore this is a very ineffective way of dealing with the problem as it sounds like a scare tactic and a shot in the dark which you hope will have the desired effect. Still it is a little more appropriate than telling his boss.

5. Based on the above, the right approach generally would be to:
   - Approach the patient to reason with him (B)
   - If this does not work, involve his wife (C)
   - If this still does not work, then notify the DVLA (D)

The other two options (threatening letter and notifying the boss) come last in that order as they are least effective.

Note on option E
If the letter had stated that you would report him to the DVLA "if the patient *persisted to drive* despite your warnings", then E would come between C and D. However, the current wording is too vague to place it high on the list.

Note on confidentiality
In the above answer, we mentioned DVLA guidelines. Although there is no compulsory need to be aware of these guidelines, it is of great help to be familiar with some of the guidelines that could be used for common scenarios. In any case, the same conclusions could be reached from first principles. To breach confidentiality you must be satisfied (and be able to demonstrate in court if need be) that the benefits of breaching confidentiality outweigh the disadvantages to the patient. In this particular instance, the patient represents a danger to the public and, therefore, once you have exhausted all avenues within the confidential environment (i.e. by discussing the issue with the patient over a reasonable period of time) then you may consider that there is value in breaching confidentiality.

Once you have made the decision to breach confidentiality, you should ask yourself who would be of most help to achieve the desired result. In this case, there would be value in involving the patient's wife before going to the DVLA. In fact, the wife is most likely already aware of the patient's condition anyway so it may not constitute a breach of confidentiality after all. The only concern would be the extent to which you would be affecting your relationship of trust with the patient; but any problem will be outweighed by the benefit to the public at large.

SCENARIO 7

ANSWER: 1:B – 2:A – 3:D – 4:C – 5:E

1. There are occasions when you will be required to make an effort to attend late work meetings and your seniors will expect you to make an effort to attend them, within reason. In this particular question, it is clearly stated that you have been told about the meeting just as you were about to leave your shift and therefore your seniors should be able to understand that you may not be able to make it at such short notice, particularly if you have a valid reason. After all, there may be other colleagues who will be on study leave or on annual leave and may not be able to make it either. Therefore, E will be ranked as the least appropriate. You will go to your dinner.

2. The issue now is to determine in what circumstances you will be leaving your workplace. This is testing your teamwork ability:

   - Option D (the nurse). Why involve her since she is probably not even going to the meeting. (Remember, this is a junior doctors teaching session.) This will place the responsibility on her to pass on a message that she could not care less about, on a topic that she knows nothing about.

   - Option A (the junior doctor). This is better. You are involving a relevant member of the team and you are offering your apologies.

   - Option B (the organiser). This is the most proactive option. Not only are you discussing the matter with the person who will know best, you are also finding out about the nature of the meeting. This will also help you identify ways in which you can keep up to date with what was discussed.

3. We are now left with one option to analyse: option C (slipping away). Although you might find that it saves you a lot of hassle in the short term (it saves you having to justify there and then why you have to leave), you will find that people will be wondering what has happened to you. The uncertainty surrounding your departure, particularly if one team member remembers telling you about the meeting, could develop into resentment towards you and this is bad news. In addition, the option says that you would consider lying when asked about your departure, which is really not a good idea in terms of keeping a clean image and proving your integrity. For these reasons, it has to be worse than involving the nurse. Both cause a problem relating to poor teamwork but, in the case of C, you are treating the whole team badly (as opposed to simply abusing the nurse's kindness).

Important note
Some of you may have ranked the options as BADEC rather than BADCE (i.e. you may feel that slipping away unnoticed is worse than letting your partner down). This would be also acceptable and you may get partial marks for this.

Similarly, if you felt compelled to attend the teaching session rather than going out with your partner (i.e. BEADC), you may also get partial marks. This would demonstrate a strong commitment to your career, but may be slightly misplaced in relation to your need for a good work-life balance, particularly as the scenario makes no mention of the level of importance of the meeting. If the scenario said that the meeting was crucial to your job, then you would have to give up going out in favour of attending the meeting.

This illustrates how the same scenario can be looked at in different lights, thus leading to different rankings. In this case, the ideal answer recognises that, although work is important, you must be able to put it in perspective in relation to other priorities, particularly if the issue at stake is a simple teaching session.

SCENARIO 8

ANSWER: C, D, F

1. Option A is not wrong but it is a little premature (it will not be immediate or in the short term). The question asks for "immediate" action. Calling the GMC may come at a much later stage if the colleague presents a real danger to patients. For the time being, all we know is that a bag of marijuana has fallen out of his bag! The road to the GMC notification is not that quick. If the GMC needs to be involved, it will not be down to you to involve them anyway but down to the Clinical Director or the Medical Director. Your role is to inform a senior.

2. B is just as bad as A. If the police need to be called, it will be by a hospital manager or someone in charge after initial investigation (also not immediate). You are hardly going to get on the phone to the police as soon as you see the bag.

3. E is a bit naïve. Of course he will give you his reassurance. He might even tell you it was planted there by a vindictive love rival! Telling him that you will keep quiet if he gets rid of the evidence is unacceptable anyway. There is a problem that needs to be looked into (and which may or may not have an impact on patient safety in the long run) so you cannot ignore it.

4. G is a bit strong, though not entirely inappropriate; however, there are other people between you and the Clinical Director and you should use them (particularly if they are in other options – like the Registrar in option F or a Consultant).

5. This leaves us with the three correct options, which are also the most sensible ones. Option D (discussing the issue with your colleague) should really be your starting point. Because of the possible impact on patient safety you ought to discuss the matter with a senior colleague that you can trust (option F – the Registrar) and, as a friend and doctor, it would be wise to advise your colleague to seek help before his drug problem escalates (option C).

Note on option C

Some people may argue that C is not appropriate because the colleague does not necessarily have a drug problem (he might just be supplying the drug to others, or maybe just carrying it for someone else). This may indeed be the case; however, if we look at all the remaining options (excluding D and F which are not controversial), then C is the most appropriate and the most sensible.

Make sure that you always choose the number of options asked for in the wording of the questions. The question is not "What are the appropriate options" but the "MOST APPROPRIATE". They want three, give them three.

Important note

If you have answered D, F and G, you may be eligible for partial marks. Option G (reporting to the Clinical Director) is not inappropriate per se but is less appropriate than other options. You may consider reporting to the Clinical Director in the absence of your Registrar or if you have substantial worries about your colleague. The reason why G does not appear in the "benchmark" answer is that the question was designed to test not only your integrity in reporting potentially unfit colleagues to a senior, but your ability to relate to and support a colleague in difficulty. This is illustrated by C.

Any other combination would not score anything.

SCENARIO 9

ANSWER: B, C, G

1. Option A: Going to the GMC will be a little premature without any kind of preliminary investigation and without giving the Consultant an opportunity to change. The matter should be first handled at local level and only escalated to GMC level by your seniors if the Consultant continues to present a danger to patients despite their best efforts to resolve the situation. At your level, your concern should be to ensure that someone senior to you whom you can trust is aware of the situation (hence why C is appropriate). You would only ever consider going to the GMC yourself if none of your seniors acted appropriately in relation to the matter at hand.

2. Option B: Since the Consultant is "obviously" drunk there is a chance that the clinic may need to be cancelled. At the very least, some of the appointments will need to be cancelled whilst others will be seen by other doctors. The wording here is quite vague ("Discuss cancelling the clinic session"), which makes it appropriate. If the wording had been stronger (such as "Tell the manager to cancel the clinic") then it may not have been appropriate as you might have needed to consider alternatives first.

3. Option C: As mentioned above, and as mentioned in the GMC's *Good Medical Practice*, you must involve a senior colleague that you can trust. As a rule you should consider going first to your Registrar, then another Consultant, then the Clinical Director. Going too high too quickly may mean that you are overreacting. It may also make your seniors feel undermined if you are not giving them the opportunity to act before going to their boss. Since the only option here is to see a Consultant then it would be appropriate.

4. Options D, E and F are all unacceptable. If the Consultant is "obviously" drunk, there is no way that you would allow him to see patients, whether you are with him or he is with a chaperone; and certainly not on his own. Not only is it likely to attract complaints from patients, it may also make them lose faith in the Trust. You could get sacked for letting this happen.

5. Option G is over the top for the time being, particularly as the Consultant has not actually seen patients yet, but it is not a totally wrong answer (it could be considered appropriate). So far we have only identified B and C as appropriate and, out of all other possibilities, G is the only remaining appropriate option (since A is really a remote possibility and D, E and F are unsafe or pose a strong reputation risk).

SCENARIO 10

ANSWER: 1:D – 2:E – 3:A – 4:B – 5:C

1. Many people think that it is illegal to prescribe for friends and family. This is not entirely correct. The GMC guidance is that "Wherever possible, you should avoid providing medical care to anyone with whom you have a close personal relationship." In practice you must distinguish between a one-off event that deals with a minor issue (such as a prescription for an inhaler) and a long-term doctor-patient relationship or an involvement with a major condition. There are examples of GPs who were suspended or struck off for caring a bit too much for their friends and family but we are not talking about such things here. Therefore E is not to be totally avoided.

2. You must look at the practicality of your answers and also at how far you are prepared to go to help your friend. There is a compromise to be reached between being friendly and being helpful. As a first port of call, it is always best and safest to send anyone to their GP (unless it is a real emergency, which this is not). Therefore, D should come first.

3. Look at the practicality and look at who is inconvenienced by each option:
   - Option A inconveniences him and A&E.
   - Option B inconveniences you and A&E (and why can't he go to A&E himself anyway? He has to take responsibility for his actions and play his part in resolving the issue for himself).
   - Option C could cause problems on the ward, as taking an inhaler from the ward effectively means taking an inhaler that was reserved for one of your patients.
   - Option E inconveniences you and is probably the quickest thing to do.

Therefore, once you have tried the GP option, it is simplest, friendliest and quickest to write him a one-off prescription for his inhaler (on the basis that it is a one-off and that the prescription is in respect of a "safe" drug in his case). It will also mean that he will have to pay for it as a private prescription and therefore it won't take advantage of the NHS.

The order of the remaining options is purely in the order of the most to least convenient.

Important note
You would also score marks for ranking the options as DAEBC (preferring to send him to A&E rather than prescribing yourself – which is probably overdoing it on the safety angle considering that he is only after an inhaler). There are times when you can be both realistic and safe at the same time. In practice, if you felt uncomfortable prescribing for a friend or a member of your family, you should seek advice and assent from a senior colleague (preferably a Consultant) so that someone above you is aware of the situation. By being open about the process, you will avoid sneaky accusations.

SCENARIO 11

ANSWER: 1:D – 2:B – 3:A – 4:C – 5:E

The key to this question is to identify how effective each option will be in resolving the matter and how sensitive your approach is. We will look at each option in reverse order of appropriateness.

1. Option E (keeping records) might sound good if you ever have to make a case to a senior colleague later on but it really feels like you are spying on your colleague and not addressing anything. Watching and waiting (for what?!) is also counterproductive as it almost implies that you hope someone else will do your dirty work for you. It is the worst option.

2. Option C (approach your colleague) might sound good because it gives the feeling that at least you are dealing with the colleague and not going straight away to a senior colleague, but the tone is very patronising. Your colleague might have personal problems that are causing the delay and C gives no indication that you have an understanding, or are trying to gain an understanding, of what these might be. Telling your colleague off will only create conflict. If someone needs to reprimand him, it will have to be someone more senior than him.

3. Option A (telling their senior) is a bit better because you are involving someone who can make a difference and they will try to get to the bottom of the problem with your colleague. This will include investigating any particular problem that may be causing the delay. You might not find out by yourself what is causing the delay but at least someone will and the problem should get resolved. There are other things that you can do though before you get to this stage.

4. Option B (discussing with other juniors) is slightly better because at least you are trying to see if the team has any ideas about the reasons behind the delay and whether there are solutions that can be found. Your other colleagues will undoubtedly also be affected by his late arrivals and therefore it makes sense to discuss the matter with them. Please note that this option is only ranking high because it mentions "junior doctors". If it mentioned "nurses" instead, then it would have no impact whatsoever and could be considered as gossip. It would therefore rank much lower.

5. Option D is the most helpful and therefore the highest ranked option. It is seeking to resolve the matter in a helpful and supportive manner.

SCENARIO 12

ANSWER: 1:C – 2:D – 3:A – 4:E – 5:B

1. The issue here is that you want to ensure that patients are safe at all times but you also want to try not to ruin your entire evening for the sake of a patient who should really be handled by someone else if possible. Therefore your approach will be to show a helpful attitude but also to ensure that the system works the way that it should work. In particular, you might have been asked to review a patient (no one said it was urgent!) but, since you are leaving your shift, surely the SHO on call is the one who should be handling this and who should be available to handle such matters (otherwise you will spend your entire days at the hospital).

    Against this background, you also have to consider that, as a junior doctor, you have responsibilities (hence why asking a Consultant to take over will not rank high for a routine case). You also have to consider the patient safety element (hence why seeing the patient quickly is not a good idea – you never know, it may end up taking much longer than you thought it would take).

2. Your first approach should be to encourage the team to function the way it should. This means getting your colleague to trace the on call SHO (C). If he is too busy for that, you would consider doing it yourself (D); the reason being that it is really the on call SHO's job to deal with the patient and not yours. The primary responsibility to delegate to the on call SHO is your colleague's, not yours.

    Some of you may find that this is not a good team playing approach, but in fact it is. It is about defining boundaries and not creating confusion by going into someone else's territory. Imagine if you were the SHO on call and you found out that another doctor has been seeing some of your patients without telling you! This could be embarrassing for you as well as unsafe for your patients.

3. If the on call SHO is not available then we are now faced with three remaining options:
    - Giving the patient to the Consultant (E)
    - Seeing him yourself (A)
    - Seeing him quickly (B)

Giving the patient to the Consultant will place you in a bad light. Option E says "Tell your Consultant". This makes it a direct command rather than a request for assistance. If the option was worded as "Ask the Consultant if he would not mind seeing the patient" then it would rank higher. It should be down to your colleague to tell the Consultant anyway, not down to you. You will therefore have to see the patient yourself.

Seeing the patient quickly is simply unsafe, which makes it the worst option. Once you have seen him, he may need further care which will take you longer to organise. What would you do if, once you have seen the patient, you need to stay behind? We are back to square one. In addition, B says that your family will be waiting for you in the waiting room during that time. This is bad news as they will be a constant reminder for you that you are late and this will bring extra pressure onto you.

SCENARIO 13

ANSWER: 1:C – 2:E – 3:D – 4:A – 5:B

In this question, you need to ensure the safety of the patient, whilst minimising the impact on your colleagues.

- Option C is both safe for the patient and convenient for the team. It will only inconvenience one single colleague.

- Option E sounds like a good idea though it could be embarrassing for your colleague if he is not well prepared. Still, it is a safe option, it ensures that the team gets their session and only one colleague is inconvenienced.

- Option D is very safe but will inconvenience everyone in the team. Also, you cannot cancel educational meetings every time there is an emergency otherwise no one would ever get trained. Still, it is better than just slipping away (at least people know what is going on and where things stand) and therefore will need to rank higher than A.

- Option A is very safe for the patient but awful for your colleagues who will be sitting around wondering what is going on.

- Option B is the most unsafe of all. The scenario says that it is an emergency call.

Interview Skills Consulting

SCENARIO 14

ANSWER: 1:B – 2:A – 3:C – 4:E – 5:D

1. Option D is a non-starter You simply cannot ignore such an important issue. Your colleague may lose his job as a result of this but, more importantly, patients may be placed in danger because of his addiction. Option D therefore has to come last.

2. All the other options involve reporting the matter but in various circumstances. When faced with such a choice, it sometimes helps to rewrite the options in a clearer, more concise manner:
   - A: Report after telling your colleague
   - B: Report after giving the colleague a chance to address the matter by himself
   - C: Report without telling the colleague
   - E: Report only if you have concerns about his performance.

   E is potentially unsafe as you should not just be concerned about his current performance but also future performance. Your colleague might be fine for now but his addiction might escalate and spiral out of control. Will you wait until he kills a patient to act?

   Out of the other three, the order is fairly obvious: B, A, C.

SCENARIO 15

ANSWER: A, B, C

1. Potentially, the patient is asking you to help him commit insurance fraud. So there is absolutely no way you will delete the information from the notes. That means that D and E are not suitable and that C is suitable. If you ever received a court order asking to see the notes, your integrity would be questioned (remember how Dr Shipman altered his records!).

2. Option A is appropriate because, unless the patient has consented, you will not be able to give any information to the insurance company. It is appropriate because you need to be absolutely clear about the boundaries. The insurance company may subsequently refuse to give the patient any insurance but this will be the patient's problem for refusing to give consent in the first place. (Note that option A cannot be generalised. There are cases where you can divulge information to a third party without the patient's consent, most often when there is a danger of serious harm or death to others, e.g. child abuse).

3. Option F is not correct. Unless you have the patient's consent, you cannot reveal the information. Saying the opposite to the patient would just be telling a lie and would be unethical.

4. Option B is appropriate as, although you may never get consent from the patient to reveal information, you should always notify him whenever you are considering breaching confidentiality. Making this clear will reassure the patient without compromising your integrity. In reality, you would not seek to breach the patient's confidentiality voluntarily in this case. But you can envisage a scenario whereby the insurance company seeks a court order to obtain information from the GP (e.g. to check on a claim), in which case you would be forced to reveal any information the court order is asking for. Saying otherwise would mislead the patient.

5. Option G would be suitable only if you contacted the insurance company without naming the patient, say to ask for advice about whether they actually care about this type of information. As soon as you name him, you are breaching confidentiality in an unacceptable context.

SCENARIO 16

ANSWER: 1:D – 2:A – 3:C – 4:B – 5:E

1. Whenever you are confronted with the issue of a gift given by a patient, you must look at the nature of the gift, the circumstances surrounding the gift and the impact that a refusal would have on the doctor-patient relationship. Your main concern will be to ensure that you are not being bribed by the patient and that the situation cannot be construed as bribery. On the other hand, you do not want the refusal of a gift to affect the doctor-patient relationship negatively.

2. In this particular example, the amount of the gift is unusually high, particularly in view of the short-term relationship that you have had with the patient. The wording of the question goes out of its way to emphasise a detachment (short admission, only contact was during ward rounds, patient not expected to come back). Therefore it would make sense to refuse the gift, at least in the first instance.

3. There are two options to do this: D which is polite and also shows a degree of care and empathy, and A which is a bit more bureaucratic but still acceptable. Therefore the first two most suitable actions must be D and A in that order.

4. We are now left with three options to accept the gift, with different contexts:

   - Option E (keeping quiet) has to be the least appropriate. In fact it is verging on unethical and dishonest (and might actually expose you to blackmail from the patient in the worst possible scenario).

   - Giving the gift to your loved one (B) might sound like a good idea but is still for personal gain. It is not as good as using the money for the good of everyone on the ward. After all, the gift was for care given to the patient and therefore rendered by the whole ward. Also giving the gift to the team will make it less likely to be construed as bribery. It is also an excellent demonstration of selflessness and teamwork. Therefore C is more appropriate than B.

SCENARIO 17

ANSWER: 1:D – 2:B – 3:E – 4:A – 5:C

1. The situation is tricky because on one hand you must try to respect the confidentiality of the patient but on the other hand it is not a very practical thing to do if the person he wants to keep in the dark is actually working on the ward where he is staying. In particular, you will want to make sure that the care of the other patients is not compromised by the issue (bearing in mind that the safety of the other patients will always be more important than the confidentiality of one patient). You also have to make sure that you do not give in to patients too easily, particularly if their requests appear unreasonable.

2. Based on the above, it seems sensible to try to reach a compromise with the patient in order to avoid any disruption. Option D explores the reasons behind the patient's request and constitutes the most appropriate action. You might find that his fears are unfounded or that, simply by reassuring him about the team's professionalism, he will accept having the nurse around.

3. Option B is then the second most suitable because it looks after the patient's confidentiality without disturbing any team member (or not much anyway). However, it is not as good as D, which at least attempts to eliminate the constraint of confidentiality in a diplomatic way.

4. Once you have done your best to sort out the situation without disturbance, either by reasoning with the patient or by issuing directives to the team, then you are left with three options:
    - Option A: tell the patient to put up with it (not necessarily a bad idea but could create problems).
    - Option E: transfer the patient to a different part of the ward. Good idea too and better than A; at least you are doing something concrete about the problem, with limited disturbance.
    - C: Tell the nurse to take some time off – unthinkable. She must have better things to do with her annual leave than to avoid patients!

Telling the patient to put up with the situation is not something that you should dismiss outright, however rude it sounds. However, in practice, you should be able to demonstrate that you have taken reasonable steps to maintain their confidentiality before giving up. This could include taking the patient to another ward. It could also include asking the nurse to work in a different ward for a while, though you ought to think twice about doing this as it may have an impact on patient care. In any case, it does not include sending the nurse away on holiday. If you ever need to tell a patient that there is little choice, then you should do so in a diplomatic manner.

Important note
You would score partial marks for answering DEBAC instead of DBEAC.

SCENARIO 18

ANSWER: 1:D – 2:E – 3:B – 4:C – 5:A

1. In a question like this, it is easy to jump to conclusions. Some may think that the Consultant is behaving inappropriately with the patient; others may think that there must be a good reason for his behaviour. After all, he may have been reassuring a patient who was distraught. Never ignore the issue, but equally you don't want to take drastic action until you have got your facts right.

2. Option A (doing nothing and making assumptions) is the worst option. If there is a problem, even potentially, you simply cannot ignore it.

3. Option C (reporting to the Clinical Director) is a possibility but it is quite strong. You would have to have reasonable concerns about the situation before you can go to the Clinical Director and therefore there are steps that you should take before seeing him. The fact that it ranks fourth does not mean that it is a wrong thing to do. It is just not as appropriate as some of the other options given the scenario and its ambiguities.

4. The three remaining options (B, D and E) are all about finding out more about the situation and seeking advice. They are therefore preferred over the other two.
    *   D is your preferred option because it enables you to discuss the situation with the Consultant in a non-confrontational manner.

    *   E comes next because you can get a different perspective from an appropriate trusted colleague. He may know the Consultant's manner with patients more than you do and might think that it is more likely to be appropriate for that Consultant than not. On the other hand, he might have come across complaints from other people before and can make a more informed decision than you can. The fact that he is running the clinic next door also means that the advice will be immediate, which is an advantage.

- B comes third because sending the patient out would be quite a brave thing to do, especially if nothing untoward was happening. If the patient was simply being reassured by the Consultant, the Consultant and the patient might find your actions a little bit offensive. You would need to think twice before doing this because you could irritate your Consultant and the patient (hence why it comes third) but it might still be an appropriate action to take if it means that it can highlight a real problem.

Do not jump to conclusions too quickly

Generally speaking, most doctors conduct themselves ethically. If you notice something strange, there is usually a good explanation for it and you should avoid jumping to conclusions too quickly. It does not mean that you have to ignore warning signs, but that you should take a gradual approach to make sure that you do not create more problems than there were in the first place. Explore the facts as appropriately as you can before escalating the matter further.

Gauge the level of appropriateness of the physical contact

The question talks about a Consultant with his arms around the shoulder of a patient. Although you should avoid physical contact with patients if possible, there may be situations where such behaviour could be accepted. If you are given a question with a more suggestive wording (such as a Consultant in an embrace with a patient or kissing a patient), then your approach should be a bit less subtle since the breach of duties will be more obvious.

SCENARIO 19

ANSWER: 1:B – 2:C – 3:A – 4:D – 5:E

1. This is a difficult set of options. The first task is to eliminate the options which do not deal with the problem:

    - Option E: it is true that your colleague should learn how to handle such situations in future but she is not going to learn by seeing this particular patient there and then. If she was reduced to tears by the experience she will not be the best doctor for this patient. This is an issue of personal safety but also of her fitness to practise with this particular man (i.e. she might not be thinking clearly).

    - Option D is a little more difficult to spot. Seeing him yourself sounds like the right thing to do but it is the second part of the sentence which should make you rank it low. Rearranging his appointments so that he is seen early in the list will certainly reduce the likelihood of future delays for him. However, it may be practically difficult to arrange and will impact negatively on other patients. Ultimately, this option ranks very low because it effectively rewards his actions and condones his behaviour, which is just unacceptable. Option D therefore ranks fourth.

2. You are now faced with the three remaining options which are all attempting to sort out the problem safely and without giving in to the patient:

    - Option A: send the patient home, cancelling his appointment. This sounds like revenge and will probably infuriate the patient even more.

    - Option C: get him to see another doctor or to come back some other time. This is more proactive in sorting out the problem than A but it unfairly places the problem with another doctor.

    - Option B: see him yourself and explain that his behaviour was unacceptable. This is the best option since you are dealing with the patient's behaviour as well as ensuring that he gets seen, thereby not aggravating the situation further.

ISCMEDICAL
Interview Skills Consulting

SCENARIO 20

ANSWER: 1:B – 2:D – 3:C – 4:A – 5:E

1. Option E (sending the patient home) is just plain wrong. He has already come to see you with chest pains and you have done nothing. He would be better off going to A&E if it is not improving. This is just hoping for the best. It is the most unsafe and least appropriate option.

2. Option A (searching for the instructions) is also unsafe because it is wasting time, though at least you are attempting to find a solution and not rejecting responsibility for the patient. If you find the instructions then you will have to read them too, assuming that they can be interpreted quickly.

3. Option C is neither ideal nor totally wrong. It might work but there is a risk attached to it. Still it is better than wasting your time finding instructions that may not exist.

4. Options B and D are the two most appropriate options because they ensure that patient safety is not compromised. Out of the two, it is obviously preferable to see if the nurse can do the ECG rather than send the patient to A&E. She might appear busy with a patient but she might also be able to leave the patient on his own for a few minutes.

SCENARIO 21

ANSWER: B, C, D

1. There is clearly a patient safety angle here and a situation which is very serious as the nurse put a patient in danger for purely selfish reasons. Therefore option A (waiting for another incident) seems a weak option. B seems a more reasonable approach which enables you to discuss the specific event with the management team and agree on any disciplinary matters.

2. Before you can discuss the event with the management team, you will need to gather some information (D). In particular, there may have been specific circumstances that led the nurse to behave in such an odd manner. Maybe she is experiencing depression or she is unhappy at work. It is not an excuse for her behaviour, but gaining some insight will help address the problem more effectively.

3. There is also clearly an issue of training as it is not practical that only one person should know how to use the machine. Therefore C is a strong candidate.

4. This gives us B, C and D as the most likely candidates, with A having been rejected as too weak for the circumstances. What about the others?

   - Going to the PCT (E) is premature since the matter has not been handled internally. Therefore it is not as appropriate as other more pressing matters such as organising training to ensure that such an incident does not reoccur. Even if you went to the PCT, the head is certainly not the right person to contact about it.

   - Writing to the patient (F) looks like a good idea. However, (i) it may be more appropriate to ask him to come for a discussion and (ii) ensuring that the incident does not reoccur is more important than writing to the patient. This could be the fourth most appropriate answer if you were allowed four. But you are not!

- Warning your colleagues by email (G) is simply unhelpful. It isolates the nurse and builds tension within the team. It creates a big team playing problem and does not help create a safer environment.

SCENARIO 22

ANSWER: 1:C – 2:B – 3:A – 4:D – 5:E

1. The main issue in this scenario is that you need to determine the woman's wishes and that she cannot express them in a way that would satisfy you. The father is able to act as an interpreter but you cannot necessarily rely on a close family member to interpret reliably for her in such a situation. You might also need to examine the woman and it will be difficult if the father is present. All in all, your preferred choice should be to talk to the woman with an interpreter in a non-threatening environment and C is therefore the best.

2. With C gone, B is your next best choice as you are still able to get the information safely from the woman's mouth through the interpreter, though this time there is a risk that she may be influenced by her father's presence.

3. Out of A, D and E:

    -   Option A is your next best choice. That is really your only alternative in the absence of an interpreter (unless a nurse or someone in your practice can interpret too, but this is not an option).

    -   Option D is just unhelpful as you would not be able to determine whether that new person is any less of a threat than the father.

    -   Option E is unsafe as you would never be able to determine whether she actually understands what you are telling her.

Important note
You would score partial marks for answering CBDAE instead of CBADE.

ANSWER: 1:B – 2:C – 3:D – 4:E – 5:A

1. This is an old lady whom you know well who offers you a small gift with no obvious bad intentions. So there is no reason to refuse the gift. In fact, refusing the gift may upset the patient and may negatively affect the doctor-patient relationship. Hence, A and E will come last, with E being slightly better as, at least, it gives you an opportunity to discuss what would have been the right thing to do and to learn from the experience.

2. B is the most appropriate option because the nature and value of the gift are appropriate in view of the ongoing relationship that you have with the patient. The other two options for accepting the gift are:

   - Option C: inform the practice manager. If you really feel that the gift is a problem for you, then this is a good way to alleviate your problems of conscience.

   - Option D: tell the patient that it must be the last time. It is a bit patronising and unnecessary given the nature of the gift, the frequency and the circumstances surrounding the gift. Because of this, it is less appropriate than C.

SCENARIO 24

ANSWER: 1:A – 2:D – 3:C – 4:B – 5:E

1. It is best not to jump to conclusions, and to get your facts right first. Hence, A is the most appropriate. You never know: your colleague might have had a perfectly good reason to perform the examination but simply failed to record it.

2. Option D (seeking advice from trusted senior colleagues) is also a good idea as it ensures that you are doing the right thing and it also enables you to address the issue without being too formal to start with. It will help establish the facts before you can take the matter further. However, it would be inappropriate to go to a senior colleague without identifying first whether there is a real cause for concern or a real doubt. You cannot do this without having any details about the nature of the problem; therefore it comes second in order of appropriateness.

3. Options A and D are the most appropriate options because there is uncertainty about whether the examination was genuine and therefore a graduated approach is required in order to get the facts right. The three remaining options are harsher in their approach and present some flaws:

    ▪ Option C is failing to get any information from the patient and involves reporting to the Clinical Director straight away. This is not necessarily a bad move, and you might consider it once you have raised the issue more informally with other senior colleagues first (D).

    ▪ Option B is more or less telling the patient that the colleague is guilty; it is therefore inappropriate. If the patient has been the victim of an unscrupulous doctor, then you would need to have a discussion with your seniors first before approaching the patient about the matter. You cannot jump to conclusions so quickly and tell the patient that the examination might constitute an assault without getting all the facts. The best that you can do in the first instance is to tell the patient that you will look into it and get back to them.

- Option E is worse than B because it is ignoring the hierarchy within your team and launching the full system against him when there may not be a cause for concern. It is not your role to go to the GMC unless your seniors fail to act appropriately. In addition, before the case can go to the GMC, it will have to go through the local complaints procedure; hence E must follow B in the order of appropriateness.

Important note
You would score partial marks for answering ACDBE instead of ADCBE.

SCENARIO 25

ANSWER: D, F, G

1. The fact that your colleague has Hepatitis C is only an issue if he is performing procedures where he is exposing his patients to a risk. Therefore, unless you believe that he performs risky procedures, you have no reason to intervene. This makes D one of the appropriate actions.

2. Option A is not an option because, even if you noticed that your colleague performed risky procedures, you would report the matter to one of your senior colleagues and not to Personnel/Medical Staffing.

3. Option B is just rubbish. A vaccine against Hepatitis C virus does not currently exist.

4. Option C is not appropriate because you would not report to a senior colleague unless he performed risky procedures (D).

5. Option E is not appropriate because it is not the role of the senior sister to spy on your colleague. She is not responsible for his actions.

6. F and G are both appropriate because they encourage your colleague to take responsibility for the situation, to seek advice from appropriate sources and to raise the matter himself with senior colleagues so the team can identify how to deal with the issue.

Note

In practice, you would remind your colleague that he should steer clear of risky procedures and encourage him to go to Occupational Health for advice (and not for vaccination!). You should also encourage him to discuss the situation with his seniors, so that they are aware of the issue and can support him, and with his defence union, so that he is aware of the risks to which he is exposed. His defence union will also be able to advise him about the best way to approach senior colleagues.

If you felt that your colleague posed a danger to patients, and you would need some kind of proof for that (for example if he told you that he performed risky procedures, or if someone else told you, or if you observed it), then you would need to discuss the issue with your colleague and impose on him to discuss the matter with a senior colleague. You could offer to go with him for support. If he fails to do so, then you would need to discuss the issue with seniors yourself.

SCENARIO 26

ANSWER: A, B, D

1. One important aspect to consider here is that your role is to support the secretary in getting the issue sorted out but not necessarily to sort it out for her. Hence A and B are appropriate. She has senior colleagues that she can approach to start the process.

2. Alternatively, she could also approach the HR department about it but it would not be your place to do it for her. Therefore F is not the most suitable.

3. There will be little value in confronting the Consultant directly about the issue as it would lead to confrontation. So C is not the most appropriate. G is also inappropriate as it feels like public humiliation for the Consultant in question and is unlikely to lead to any substantial result.

4. Approaching another senior colleague (D) would be more constructive as it would enable the senior team to become aware of the problem and to find a suitable way of approaching the Consultant in question (rather than the confrontational style of C).

5. Contacting the GMC (E) is just wrong unless the situation has reached such proportions that the local systems cannot handle it. It would thus not feature as one of the "most appropriate" options in such a situation.

Important note
You may score partial marks if you answered ABC instead of ABD as C is a possibility in some cases (e.g. if you know the Consultant in question well), though the outcome is fairly unpredictable.

SCENARIO 27

ANSWER: A, B, G

1. This question tests your integrity. If you have made a mistake then you must own up to it, whether it has any consequences or not.

2. Option C is not safe as you simply cannot wait until the patient has a reaction to the drug in order to take any action.

3. Option D shows that you are being honest with your team but you must also tell the patient if you have injected them with the wrong product, even if this means taking the consequences (hence why A is appropriate).

4. Option E might be open and attempting to minimise the stress on the patient but it is dishonest. It is NOT a procedure that is sometimes carried out. It is just a mistake that sometimes happens.

5. Option F blames the nurse. Whoever brought the wrong product, you are the one who injected it so you must take responsibility for your mistake. If there is a problem with the nurse then you can sort it out later with her but do not involve the patient with such interpersonal staff matters. This will look unprofessional and can reduce the patient's confidence in the medical team.

6. Option A is the most honest answer. You will just have to bite the bullet. Option B ensures that a senior colleague is informed and that the right course of action is being followed. Option G ensures that the team can learn from the incident.

SCENARIO 28

ANSWER: A, C, D

1. The simplest approach is to proceed by elimination:

   - Option G (critical incident form) is not an answer to someone who is washed out. You should complete a form whenever a critical incident occurs, regardless of how tired the doctor is. In any case, by the time you complete the form and it gets processed, he will have had plenty of time to make other mistakes. This is a red herring.

   - Option F (contacting Occupational Health) is also ineffective. Firstly, if you are going to contact someone about it, it should be one of your seniors. Secondly, Occupational Health are not responsible for that Registrar so they would not be able to do much.

   - Option E (locum through Medical Staffing). Getting a locum should not be your decision. If a locum is required to relieve the pressure on the Registrar then it should be done through the proper channels, as a result of a discussion between your Registrar and his seniors. You are interfering.

2. You are now left with A, B, C and D. All of them are possible candidates but you need to eliminate one of them. Option B stands out because it feels harsh, patronising and not very supportive in relation to the other answers. If he ends up actually placing patient safety at risk then you may resort to discussing the situation with the Consultant, but you should aim to achieve this without having to threaten the Registrar.

SCENARIO 29

ANSWER: 1:D – 2:B – 3:C – 4:A – 5:E

1. This is a really awkward situation because the patient is new and you do not want to destroy his confidence in you at the outset. On the other hand, you must also find a safe approach.

2. Option E is very unsafe. You are taking a big gamble. You can't have a patient walking around the streets with a week's worth of methadone. Some GPs who have done that in the past have ended up being struck off (it came to light when the patient took the whole dose in one go and died). It has to be the least appropriate.

3. Option A is also unsafe to the extent that it relies on the patient to tell you what their normal dose is, but it is safer than E because you are only giving one dose.

4. Having eliminated the unsafe options, we are now left with:
    - B: send the patient to A&E
    - C: Wait until the notes arrive
    - D: Call the previous GP.

    The order D, B and C seems logical. Calling the previous GP will give you a reliable way to identify the correct dose. Sending the patient to A&E is not ideal because doctors probably have better things to do there but at least it is a safe option for the patient. They can check that he is a heroin addict through a urine test and prescribe one dose. Waiting for the notes and prescribing nothing feels a bit like a cop-out but it is sometimes better than taking a risk. The patient always has the option to go to a local rehabilitation centre.

Note
Sending the patient to a local rehabilitation centre was not an option, but if it had been an option it would take precedence over sending the patient to A&E.

SCENARIO 30

ANSWER: 1:C – 2:D – 3:B – 4:E – 5:A

---

1. There is a definite problem so you cannot do nothing. Therefore option A comes last.

2. Option E (confronting the colleague at the team meeting) is the least effective of the remaining options. It will probably ensure that it never happens again but it will humiliate him and will create a problem within the team.

3. Option C: as ever, you should try to discuss the situation with the colleague first and make him realise that he has done wrong. He must understand how such behaviour affects the team and that it is not acceptable. Because there is no effect on patient safety, there may not be a need to report the matter straight away, hence why warning him is a better option.

4. Option B is harsh and does not give your colleague the opportunity to redeem himself. Because it is an issue which has affected the junior doctors (since they had to cover for him), it makes sense to address the situation as a team (D). The team can then decide how best to address the matter, whether this is by having a strong word with the colleague, or by reporting the matter to a senior colleague (particularly if it happens often!).

Important note
You may score partial marks if you answered CBDEA instead of CDBEA.

114

SCENARIO 31

ANSWER: 1:D – 2:E – 3:B – 4:C – 5:A

1. Option A: the fact that he is watching the images on his own computer makes no difference. It is the act of looking at the child pornography that matters. Therefore option A should rank last in appropriateness.

2. Options B (police), D (senior colleague) and E (HR department) are fairly easy to rank. You can start from within your team and go towards the outside. So, in order of appropriateness, you should first consider talking to a senior colleague, then HR and then the police. You do not want to undermine the people you work with, so you should always go to a senior first. If they are not available or are not doing anything about the problem, then you may consider escalating to a different level (first at Trust level, then outside). Ranking the police as the least appropriate of these three options does not mean that it is inappropriate to call them. We are simply saying that it is not necessarily your role to call them and that, before the police are called, a range of internal people (senior, HR) should be involved.

3. The main problem is with option C (sending an anonymous note) because, although it looks like you are doing something, it is rather counterproductive. You are introducing fear in your colleague (which may have an impact on his performance), you are not actually trying to resolve the fundamental problem and you are introducing a climate of suspicion within the team (he will forever be trying to identify who sent him that letter). So, essentially, you are not really doing anything useful and it is just about marginally better than doing nothing at all. The real issue here is child protection. No need to be too subtle about it.

SCENARIO 32

ANSWER: B, D, E

1. Adult pornography is not illegal. However, it would certainly be seen by both patients and staff as very unprofessional to watch it in any workplace environment, particularly a hospital, where patients can become exposed to it. Your colleague is acting unprofessionally by watching it in an inappropriate place. He is going against hospital policy, but in many ways that is his problem more than yours. However, it is likely to become a real problem if it starts to offend others, particularly patients.

2. Because it is not illegal, a gentle warning about problems the Registrar might encounter is probably the first thing that you would do. Hence B is one of the most suitable options. The issue of patient safety also cannot be ignored and therefore E is appropriate too.

3. Option G (police) is irrelevant since it is not illegal. Option C (confronting him as a group) is just humiliating when there is no need to do so. If possible, you should take a tactful approach.

4. Options A and F might become an option later on but they would need to be initiated by a senior colleague on your team if they felt that the problem needed further investigation or action. It is not for you to make such decisions.

5. This leaves us with D, which seems a sensible thing to do. If you have real concerns about someone's professionalism because of the way they act then you should feel free to approach a senior colleague about it. The senior colleague may act or they may not, but at least you have raised the issue. In the chronology of events, you would tactfully seek to sort the problem directly with the Registrar first before going to the Consultant.

SCENARIO 33

ANSWER: 1:A – 2:B – 3:C – 4:D – 5:E

1. This question is a trick question where doing nothing is actually the right thing to do! This is gossip about someone you don't know getting drunk at a Christmas party at which you were not present. Why bother...? Option A is therefore the most appropriate.

2. The rest follows in the order of escalation, i.e. the higher up you go and the more people you involve, the less suitable the option.

SCENARIO 34

ANSWER: 1:A – 2:C – 3:B – 4:D – 5:E

1. Before you do anything (and this includes reporting her), you need to get more information about the nurse's actions. There is no doubt that taking antibiotics for personal use from the trolley is unprofessional and she should also be made aware of this. Hence option A should come before you address the problem at a more senior level.

2. Writing a critical incident form (E) will achieve nothing at all. It has to be the least appropriate option as there is nothing critical about it.

3. The other options (B, C, D) involve reporting to various people. You should start with the nurse's immediate superior and escalate on the nursing hierarchy. However, going to the Director of Nursing is quite a strong action to take and, before you do this, you may want to seek advice from your own Consultant. In any case, he may be able to play a role in resolving the matter within the department rather than making a big fuss about a relatively small issue (it would be different if she were taking controlled drugs instead of antibiotics).

Important note
If the scenario stated that, as a result of the nurse's actions, the patient's health had been compromised then the ranking would be CBDEA, i.e. all options in the same order except for A, which comes last.

SCENARIO 35

ANSWER: A, C, F

1. As part of a team it is important that you show some flexibility in your relationship with your colleagues, particularly if they have requests that are not unreasonable. Do to others as you would want others to do for you! However, you should ensure that patient safety is never compromised.

2. Option D (insist he stays) seems harsh in a context where all the jobs have been done and this is a special occasion, particularly if he clears it with a senior before and if you can cover for him for the remainder of the day.

3. Option E (Medical Staffing) seems pointless since it will take time and they will only tell you to clear the matter with a senior colleague (which is option A).

4. Option B (let him slip away) is the optimum flexibility but it is not very safe. What if the Registrar needs to get hold of him urgently? Also, the Registrar or someone else may have had plans for him, thinking that he would be around, and therefore it would be best practice to let someone senior know.

5. Option G (redirecting bleep to on call) is unsafe as the on call hasn't started. In any case, if you take the responsibility to let your colleague go then you should take the problems that come with it.

6. In this context, options A, C and F seem the most logical options to retain.

SCENARIO 36

ANSWER: 1:B – 2:A – 3:C – 4:D – 5:E

1. Most people would tell you that they would just ignore it. However, since we are in a medical selection context, you could at least make an effort to see if he is okay! It does not cost much and no one could fault you for doing this. Hence B has to be the most appropriate option.

2. The truth is that you would not want to launch a full medical team after every drunk person in the street if there is no real emergency. Therefore C, D and E, which are quite involved when there is nothing to suggest an emergency, would be over the top (he is only vomiting, there is no mention of blood or anything drastic). Option A is therefore second best.

3. If you did decide to do something then E would be pointless since you are near A&E and the tramp hardly justifies monopolising an ambulance in such circumstances. Therefore E comes last.

4. After that, it is a case of choosing between taking him to A&E yourself or fetching someone from A&E to take him in. If you want to be a Good Samaritan, do it in a way that is least disturbing for your colleagues. There is no need to take an A&E member out of A&E for this. You should do it yourself.

SCENARIO 37

ANSWER: 1:D – 2:A – 3:E – 4:B – 5:C

1. Option D is the most sensible and the safest approach since you are well trained and have practice. Whether you can get away with it will very much depend on the Consultant's ego.

2. Option A is also safe (in fact this is what would happen if no one in the team had ALS training). However, it comes second to D because you are only providing basic care to the patient (albeit safe care) and not the maximum care that is provided under D.

3. Option E is unsafe because you have to wait for help and you are doing nothing in the meantime to stop an unsafe situation; but at least expert help should be quick arriving.

4. Option B is unsafe and you are not acting in the patient's best interest.

5. Option C is chaotic. Team members will get confused between mixed messages. The Consultant will be undermined and all this will build resentment. In fact, the patient is likely to be worse off than if the Consultant handled the whole event by himself (option B).

SCENARIO 38

ANSWER: C, F, H

1. Option A would only be an option if you felt that you were being bullied (in which case hospital procedures may indicate that you should complain either to a senior colleague or Human Resources). However, there are many options that you can choose before making a formal complaint. The question suggests that it is a one-off incident or a first occurrence. If it had suggested that it happened frequently then A would be a possible appropriate action; but in the absence of more details, we can leave it out.

2. Option B is not appropriate because this is a matter between the Consultant and you. By complaining to a senior nurse you are seeking support from someone who will not want to interfere in this hierarchy and who really has nothing to do with the problem. At best she can have a word with the Consultant but the Consultant will feel aggrieved that you have involved people who are unrelated to the incident.

3. Option C is non-committal and encourages you to think properly about your actions before going ahead. This should certainly feature in the list of appropriate actions. Generally, in conflict situations, it is best to step out and think with a clear head.

4. Option D is the "tit-for-tat" response and will only inflame the situation. Your Consultant probably does not realise that he is out of order and therefore any attempt to respond in a similar manner will achieve nothing. Besides, sorting out the problem in front of the patient is not the best solution. Your Consultant will never forgive you for embarrassing him.

5. Option E not only involves the patient in a conflict which is really none of their concern, but you are also undermining the Consultant's credibility at the same time. This is probably one of the worst actions that you can take in the circumstances. If you need to involve external parties, make sure you involve people who can actually help resolve the problem. The patient is not one of them.

6. Option F is a sensible course of action. If you have a problem with someone, talk to them. It may not be a nice meeting but at least they will know how you feel and they may even learn something about themselves in the process. This is the best approach to regaining a sensible working relationship with the Consultant and you may find that he respects you for this.

7. Option G is just inappropriate. To complete a critical incident form, there needs to be a critical incident, i.e. an incident that had or could have had an impact on patient care. The team must be able to learn from the incident so that a concrete solution can be implemented to prevent future occurrences. They do not deal with personality issues.

8. Option H belongs to the "Involving a third party" category, but this time your education supervisor is one of the most suitable people to involve. There are three reasons for this: (i) he is responsible for your education and the incident was part of the educational process; (ii) he is a Consultant and part of your hierarchy; (iii) he is in a position to intervene or provide advice at a relevant level.

SCENARIO 39

ANSWER: 1:D – 2:A – 3:E – 4:C – 5:B

1. We have a situation where we don't know if the colleague has had one sip or more, why they were drinking and whether they have a drink problem or just a temporary weakness. Therefore it is important to act with a degree of diplomacy.

2. On the other hand, there is an issue of fitness to practise. In the worst-case scenario, the colleague may be unsafe. In the best-case scenario, he may not be unsafe but he will smell of alcohol, which can be construed as unprofessional.

3. Options B and C both encourage you to drop the matter and are therefore the least appropriate options. In cases of alcohol intake whilst at work, you cannot ignore the patient safety aspect. Therefore dropping the matter is out of the question. Out of the two options, C is slightly better than B because at least you are warning him that you might do something in future, whilst in B you are simply giving up.

4. Options A and D are both appropriate options as you demonstrate that you understand the gravity of the situation and that you are (i) talking to your colleague about it and (ii) involving senior colleagues. D has a softer approach than A and is probably more appropriate in the circumstances described. If the question had actually said that the colleague was visibly drunk then you may have preferred the stronger approach dictated by A.

5. We know that D should be the first option and that C and B should be the bottom options. The main problem is whether A is better than E or vice versa. The dilemma is as follows: option A is slightly harsh whereas E allows you more flexibility by making you seek advice from other colleagues. On the other hand, E also means spreading rumours/gossips about your colleague, which could undermine his standing in the team.

6. The key to the dilemma is in the level of efficiency achieved by each option in helping the matter progress. In option A you are being upfront with the colleague and, with your colleague's knowledge, you are going to a relevant person who will be in a good position to discuss and resolve the matter. With option E, you are going to the rest of the team behind your colleague's back. Furthermore, those colleagues will only be able to advise you and once you have received that advice you will be on your own again to make a decision. E therefore looks attractive but will yield little, whilst A, although slightly harsh, will ensure that something gets done. It is also the more open approach of the two.

SCENARIO 40

ANSWER: A, C, E

1. Option D is not acceptable. The fact that the mistake had no impact on the outcome does not mean that you do not have to act.

2. In such a situation, the Consultant (who is ultimately responsible for the patient) should be informed. A critical incident form should also be completed as it is a mistake that could be avoided with better processes in place. An investigation into the process is required to determine where it went wrong and how future occurrences can be prevented. Option A is therefore the most suitable option. Option B can be dismissed because you should not wait until mistakes have been made several times to raise the issue and/or take corrective action.

3. Informing senior Trust managers (G) is not strictly relevant unless there is a serious risk of the Trust being sued as a result of the mistake (in which case it would be important that the Trust lawyers are informed as soon as possible). If the relatives had threatened to sue, for example, then you would need to go to your Clinical Director as soon as possible so that he can involve the relevant managers. In the context of this particular scenario we are not told of any particular threat and the relevant Trust authorities will be informed via the critical incident form, which should be enough given the circumstances.

4. Informing the rest of the team (C) is an important factor because they will need to learn from the situation at an individual level. It will not have any impact on the patient who died but the team will become a lot more aware of the type of issues that can arise. They can then play an important role in implementing changes within the team to make sure that such a mistake does not reoccur.

5. Options E and F both raise the issue of talking to the relatives. The options imply that the Consultant was not present at the time of the incident and the scenario states explicitly that the relatives are upset (though we are not sure whether they are upset only because of the death of the patient or because they became aware that a mistake was made). Waiting until the Consultant comes back could take a while and it would be careless to let the relatives wait around for any length of time. If there are sensitive issues to discuss, you could always let them know that you would like to talk to your Consultant before going into detail but, in the absence of the Consultant, you will need to meet with the relatives sooner rather than later (unless, of course, there is a Registrar around, but this is not an option here). Option E is therefore more appropriate than F.

SCENARIO 41

ANSWER: 1: C – 2:B – 3:D – 4:A – 5:E

1. The question says that the patient is 17. She is therefore technically still a minor (being under the age of 18) and you have a child protection responsibility.

2. This scenario deals with a sad situation but there is no hint that you must deal with it at this very minute. Therefore, in doubt, and given that you have time in front of you, you should seek advice from other members of your team before doing anything. If you are about to breach a patient's confidentiality, it is always best to make sure that you have got it absolutely right. Therefore option C is ranked at the top.

3. Your duty will be to protect the patient. Had the patient been over 18 and with old small bruises then you could argue that the onus would be on her to make a decision for herself and that all you could do would be to provide advice. However, the scenario is quite clear that she is only 17 and that the bruises are severe. Therefore there is some justification for breaching confidentiality to ensure that she is not placed in danger physically, socially or mentally. Options B and D are both possible candidates. Option B is very harsh but you are breaching confidentiality with the patient's full knowledge. Option D takes a softer approach which is more in line with what one would expect, but it finishes badly by mentioning that you will go behind the patient's back. Although not strictly unethical, it should certainly be avoided if possible as it could impair the relationship and trust that the patient has with you. Therefore B, although harsher, is more suitable, closely followed by D.

4. It remains to allocate A and E to the last two places, which means having to decide whether it would be best to have a discussion with the patient's partner or to do nothing. Going to the patient's partner could have disastrous consequences. He may feel threatened and, given that we are told that he is a violent criminal who takes drugs, one could ask what would be achieved by such a discussion other than more trouble for the patient. We can therefore conclude that, on balance, it would be safer for the patient if you did nothing than if you had a discussion with her partner. By giving her time to reflect, she may well come to a safer decision by herself later on. This places options A and E in fourth and fifth position respectively.

Note
This is a rare example when doing nothing may actually be better than taking an action which, on balance of probabilities, could prove very detrimental to the patient.

You may score partial marks if you have answered CDBAE instead of CBDAE.

SCENARIO 42

ANSWER: A, D, F

1. One of the key factors in this scenario is the fact that the problem is recurrent and that the Registrar has a fairly casual approach to it. It is a clear potential conflict situation where one of the parties is having problems recognising that there is an issue and therefore fails to take steps to address it. In dealing with such issues, there are a number of factors that you need to consider:

    - Guaranteeing patient safety

    - Trying to sort it out directly with the individual if you can

    - Escalating the process to an appropriate senior if necessary

    - Minimising the impact on the team as much as you can.

2. Option D is the most appropriate of all options since you are attempting to resolve the matter in the most personal manner.

3. Option A is appropriate once you have failed to resolve the matter directly because the Consultant is responsible for patient care and he will need to be able to influence the situation so that patients are safe.

4. Option F is appropriate because the Registrar failed to review a very sick patient and therefore patient safety was compromised. There are lessons to be learnt and completing a critical incident form will assist the learning process.

5. Options B and C both advocate that the problem should be ignored but that you should compensate by asking others to step into the Registrar's shoes instead. This would probably make the patients safer to a degree as they would get a quicker review (maybe) than with the absent Registrar, but it is certainly not a guarantee. In any case, it is not a solution that can be adopted permanently.

6. Option E is inviting colleagues to gossip and introduces the notion of mistrust. This is simply not a good team playing attitude and you should be more open in your dealings with others.

7. Option G is not appropriate because a senior nurse has no direct hierarchical responsibility over the Registrar.

Note

If option B had been "Ensure that you seek help from another Registrar whenever yours is unavailable" (i.e. not making any mention that you would ignore the problem), then it would have featured amongst the most suitable options for ensuring the immediate safety of patients. The answer would then have been ABD (to an extent the critical incident form can wait, relatively speaking).

SCENARIO 43

ANSWER: 1:B – 2:C – 3:A – 4:D – 5:E

1. This question not only deals with the manner with which you handle the referral process but also about the manner with which you deal with the patient's expectations. In your answer, you should take account not only of the efficiency with which you handle the problem in a busy environment but also the impact of your actions and the reward that you are likely to get in return for the amount of effort that you put in. For example, B does not take long to do but it may actually achieve the desired effect.

2. Option A is the theoretical answer to the question in that, ideally, if the patient wants to seek a specialist opinion for what is not an emergency, he should go back to his GP and ask for a referral. However, before you do that, there are easy steps that you can take, which may resolve the problem once and for all. Your first steps would be to show the patient that you are confident (B) and, failing this, to get another colleague who is present for a second opinion (C). This will save everyone a lot of trouble if it works.

3. Option D is failing to address any of the patient's worries and is slightly dismissive. However, it does attempt to get a second opinion (if the patient can afford it or has insurance). Option E is equally dismissive but, worse, it simply postpones the problem to another day and to another doctor. By not sending the patient back to the GP or to a dermatologist then you are not actually making the matter progress. Option E therefore has to be the worst possible option, which places D in fourth position.

One of the points of the question is to get you to think about what is best for the patient as opposed to what is best for you as a doctor (within limits). By trying to resolve the problem by yourself in the first instance (i.e. without referring to others systematically) then you demonstrate initiative and also a recognition that you could actually save the patient and other doctors a lot of trouble. For example, referring the patient back to the GP may inconvenience both the GP and the dermatologist who will see the patient subsequently. A little investment of your time will save others (and the NHS) a lot of time.

SCENARIO 44

ANSWER: 1:D – 2:C – 3:B – 4:E – 5:A

1. As a junior doctor you are not entitled to speak on behalf of the Trust, however good your intentions. The press can easily misquote you or quote you out of context (even if you ask for reassurances) and you must ensure that the journalist contacts the right person. This means that option A should come last. Similarly, E comes in fourth place as it implies that you will be answering the journalist's questions.

2. Options B, C and D are all realistic options and the ranking can be determined as follows:

   - Option B is the rude option, when such an attitude is not strictly necessary. It does not reflect well on the Trust and you may find a comment in the article about no one being available for comment except for rude doctors. Since the other two options are more helpful and polite, B should come in third place.

   - Options C and D both boil down to sending the journalist to a more appropriate person; however, in D he must do the work himself to find the right person whilst in C you are doing the work for him. In this situation, it is not exactly your responsibility to do the journalist's job for him (surely your patients should take priority) and therefore you should prioritise D over C. Most Trusts have one person responsible for press enquiries and the journalist should follow the right channels.

SCENARIO 45

ANSWER: 1:B – 2:C – 3:E – 4:A – 5:D

1. Option D is dishonest and will make your work entirely useless. It has to be the worst option.

2. Three of the options refer to the way in which you would handle the data:

   - Photocopy and anonymise (B)
   - Copy on paper (C)
   - Take notes home (A)

   Option A is the worst of the three. Taking the notes away from the practice not only risks a breach of confidentiality if they were to fall into somebody else's hands; but there is also the small but possible risk that you may lose these notes for good. Option C would be acceptable in principle but rushing the exercise makes it prone to error. Option B is definitely the best option as it provides you with a reliable record together with a good protection of the patient's confidentiality. Therefore B, C and A should appear in that order from most suitable to least suitable.

3. This leaves us with the issue of option E, which should appear in third position: it is more appropriate to cancel a meeting with your supervisor about the audit than to get the data input done by taking the notes home. Your supervisor would not appreciate hearing how you got it all done on time by acting unprofessionally.

Note on option B
Many candidates would be hesitant to rank option B as first. However, the fact that the photocopies have been anonymised makes it both a professional and safe option. If B did not mention that any patient-identifiable information would be removed then you would need to consider cancelling the meeting before taking the risk of taking identifiable patient data home. In that case, the answer would be CEBAD.

Note on options A and D

Some candidates may wish to rank D as more appropriate than A since they feel that a patient's confidentiality is more important than the results of a small audit's project i.e. a few made-up data points changing the results of a whole audit is not such a bad thing in contrast to the potential disclosure of patient confidential information to an unauthorised third party.

In this case, you have to step back and think about the probability of these events occurring and their likely impact. On the face of it, creating results for 20 patients in an audit may seem insignificant; however, 20 patients may form a substantial number that can skew the results of the audit. Audits, as an essential component of clinical governance, are intended to assess and guide clinical practice. Therefore, falsifying results will undermine this and could impact negatively on future practice. On the other hand, the potential disclosure of patient information from taking notes home with you is only a potential risk if several unforeseen circumstances were to occur, e.g. your house being burgled or the notes being picked up and read by a family member. Furthermore, it is only likely to be of significance if the notes are comprehensible to a third-party and, in particular, if they knew the patient concerned.

This will always remain a conflict between the ethical principles of Justice and Autonomy; however, on balance, more damage can potentially be done by falsifying the audit.

SCENARIO 46

ANSWER: A, B, F

1. Options B and F are two obvious contenders as you would try to address the issue first with the colleague in question and then with the Consultant.

2. The problem then is that there does not seem to be any other option that would be suitable:

   ▪ Option A feels like you are rejecting responsibility.
   ▪ Option C is just pointless. Why do you need to do a survey to determine if someone has strong body odour?!
   ▪ Option D is public humiliation.
   ▪ Option E is also humiliating for the colleague though he will not feel the effect straight away. It is also difficult to see what discussions would take place at such a meeting.
   ▪ Option G is a coward's approach.

When faced with such a dilemma, you need to look at the option which is most likely to achieve a result and appears to be the least insensitive. Ultimately this problem is best addressed on a one-to-one basis with the colleague in question. Option A is best placed to achieve this (even though you are pushing the responsibility to sort it out onto the Consultant – though one may argue that this is part of his remit anyway).

SCENARIO 47

ANSWER: 1:D – 2:C – 3:B – 4:A – 5:E

1. As in most cases, it is best to sort out any situation directly with the individual concerned. However, you must ensure that the problem is handled sensitively too. Therefore D is the obvious candidate for the most appropriate response.

2. Option A (the heavy approach) is dangerous. Not only will you embarrass the receptionist in front of the other patient but you might end up looking silly too, particularly if you have misunderstood the situation. Option A is therefore likely to feature towards the bottom in order of priority.

3. Option E looks tempting because it brings an element of patient communication into the process but it is, in fact, a red herring. This is the type of incident that you want to play down. Apologising to all patients will not only embarrass the receptionist, it will also raise the profile of the incident and will certainly not help matters. Therefore E will rank last. It ranks lower than A because it maximises the receptionist's embarrassment.

4. This leaves us with B and C to rank. On the basis that the clinic manager will have influence on the receptionist and that this is not really an issue that can be ignored, C will rank higher than B.

5. To confirm that we have the right order we also need to validate the fact that B (do nothing, but talk to the clinic manager next time) is ranked higher than A (telling the receptionist to stop there and then). Such ranking suggests that it is better to let the matter lie until next time rather than risk embarrassing the receptionist in front of everyone. This makes sense since, although the matter is not trivial, it is not something that needs to be addressed there and then at the risk of the receptionist losing face or motivation for the job. Also, you may want to establish a pattern of behaviour before reporting the issue.

SCENARIO 48

ANSWER: A, B, E

1. There are two issues to consider in this scenario: your Consultant's integrity and the fact that two doctors have potentially fake CVs and therefore pose a possible danger to patients by misrepresenting themselves to future employers. The issue is further complicated by the fact that you still need to work with your Consultant and therefore need to be careful in your handling of the matter.

2. Talking to your Consultant privately would be a good start, which makes option E a good candidate. During the meeting you should ensure that you do not become an accessory to the fraudulent activity that is taking place and you will need to refuse to add the names to the publication unless these individuals have had some input into the process (option A). It would be tempting to go ahead with the publication with the extra names in for the sake of an easy life (option C) but you must think about the consequences of your own actions and also the consequences of helping two doctors fraudulently representing themselves. Whether it is a case report or a more important publication is not what the problem is. It is a matter of personal ethics and duty towards your patients and society.

3. Reporting your Consultant to the GMC will achieve little. Although his approach was unprofessional, you would need to discuss the matter with the Clinical Director first. The issue is not of extreme gravity as far as your Consultant is concerned and the Clinical Director is likely to handle the matter by himself without involving the GMC (unless this is a recurrent problem). However, you may want to contact the GMC about the two other doctors (option B) as their fraud is a potential risk to patients.

4. Checking with others (option D) sounds like a good idea but it will just be spreading rumours. In any case, if he had been trying the same trick with other colleagues, the next step would be to contact the Clinical Director and not the GMC. So, D is not suitable.

5. Warning the paper (option G) is pointless. There is little they will be able to do about it. And you may get sued by the other two doctors for slander.

SCENARIO 49

ANSWER: B, C, D

1. Agreeing to make the change (A) could lead you into great trouble (possibly being struck off). You are responsible for your own decisions and therefore the only option open to you is to refuse to make the entry (B).

2. Your next step would be to contact your defence union (C) and to make sure that you keep a note of the conversation that you had with your Consultant as you may need to testify in future.

3. Following on from that, you will need to report the matter to a senior colleague. Your Clinical Director is the obvious candidate for this (option D). Informing the GMC (F) is a little premature. If there is cause for concern, the Clinical Director may well do that but later in the process. As for informing the police (G), this is also a possible course of action but not one that you will need to take by yourself. If need be, the police will be called following a decision made at Trust level (e.g. by managers, the Medical Director, the Chief Executive) but not by you.

4. Informing the patient that a mistake has been made is a good idea and should be done. However, option E also says that you should tell the patient about the Consultant's attempt to modify the notes. If a decision is made to tell the patient about the Consultant's request then it will be made in consultation with the Trust's management (as there is a legal risk). You should stick to the clinical aspect of the work and let the managers handle any situation that has possible legal implications. This makes option E inappropriate.

SCENARIO 50

ANSWER: 1:B – 2:A – 3:E – 4:D – 5:C

1. This question is primarily about confidentiality. As a rule, you can breach the confidentiality of an adult patient in a few circumstances only, e.g. if there is a risk of serious harm or death to a third party or you are the recipient of a court order. Such exceptions are not relevant here and confidentiality must be maintained. Option C is the only option that clearly breaches confidentiality and therefore must be the least suitable option.

2. Option D is deliberately misleading since it is falsely confusing competence with confidentiality. Competence dictates whether you can take consent from a patient. Taking option D will also mislead the father. However, since this leads to a favourable outcome i.e. not divulging confidential details to him, it is the not the least suitable option. Letting the Registrar take the call would be more appropriate than misleading the father; hence option E ranks third.

3. Options A and B are suitable for the top two places. However Option A is slightly harsh and dismissive towards the father whilst B is more compassionate and is less likely to cause communication problems later on during this admission.

Note on confidentiality
Telling the father that his daughter is "fine" would not be seen as a breach of confidentiality. The term "fine" is very vague and serves to reassure the father rather than provide any meaningful information. After all, he has reasons to be concerned and if there are ways in which you can reassure him without compromising your integrity then you should use them. This assumes that the father knows that his daughter was admitted in this hospital in the first place (which the question implies). If the question said "a man is on the phone asking if his daughter is in your hospital" then you would not be able to divulge the information as you would then confirm to the father that his daughter is receiving treatment, which he wasn't aware of.

SCENARIO 51

ANSWER: 1:D – 2:B– 3:C – 4:E – 5:A

1. Three of the options relate to the same topic – the extent to which you would breach confidentiality: A, C and D.

    - Option A is clearly the least suitable option as you would blatantly breach the husband's confidentiality whilst, at the same time, not benefiting the wife in any way.

    - Option C also makes you breach confidentiality, but only on the subject of whether the husband came to see you rather than what he came to see you for. Although not best practice, this is lot more acceptable than option A, particularly if you feel that she already knows that he came or you feel that she is almost certain he did. One of the dangers with this approach is that, once you have revealed that the husband did come to see you, the wife will ask more questions about the reasons.

    - Option D is the best approach as you are ensuring that you maintain the husband's confidentiality at all costs. This is justified because all the wife needs to know is that she has an infection that needs treating, regardless of where she got it from. The rest is a matter between her and her husband.

2. Option B (asking advice from colleagues) will become an appropriate option when you realise that you are out of your depth, i.e. it should be ranked just before the option in which you start making a mistake or acting unprofessionally. We have ranked D, C and A in that order and have identified that C is slightly unprofessional because you have revealed that the husband did visit your surgery. Therefore B should rank before C.

3. Option E is an interesting one. There isn't really a conflict of interest. You can perfectly treat both patients for whatever infection they have and work on each of the two individuals to achieve joint counselling. It is also a bit melodramatic; the situation is not very extreme and, if you sent the patient to another GP, she would only start asking similar questions again. Having to register at another GP practice may also add unnecessary delay in the management of her medical condition.

    It is ranking fourth because it is not something that would achieve very much but it is still better than breaching the husband's confidentiality.

    Some may feel that options C and E should be swapped since option C divulges some information about the husband (i.e. that he has come to the surgery at all). This in itself is a breach of confidentiality. However, by stating in option E that there is a potential conflict of interest, you will also imply that there is some problem and that you are aware of information about her husband. This, on top of the upheaval of changing GP practice, will cause more problems than good.

SCENARIO 52

ANSWER: 1:A – 2:B– 3:C – 4:D – 5:E

1. This is a very serious issue which could lead to unsuitable students qualifying. It is therefore important that the problem is addressed as soon as possible. The deanery needs to investigate the extent of the problem and, if necessary, will need to write a new exam paper. In order to investigate, they will need to contact those who came into possession of the paper and therefore option A should rank as the most suitable option.

2. Option B (reporting without naming the student) would also be effective as it would raise the issue at the highest level where something can be done about it. By not naming the student, you are protecting him (which could be interpreted in many ways) but at least you are giving others in charge the power to sort the problem out. Note that there is no issue of confidentiality here. The student is not a patient. You must treat the incident sensitively but if need be you can name the culprits.

3. Option C is a feeble attempt at resolving the problem. It is almost guaranteed to fail, but at least you tried (which is not the case for the two remaining options D and E).

4. Option D (ignoring the matter) is fairly bad as there is an obvious cause for complaint here. But it is not as bad as propagating the fraud to continue by encouraging him to distribute the papers further (option E). One may think this is a good option since everyone would have access to the questions. However, you could not be sure that the papers would be distributed to everybody in the year group. Ultimately, this is a bad idea since the whole purpose of an exam is not just to test the content of the paper but to ensure that, through the process of revision, candidates have covered a significant proportion of the syllabus.

Note on ignoring problems
Doing nothing is often the worst option because in most cases you are expected to be proactive in resolving problems. However, doing something that makes things worse is obviously less appropriate than remaining passive.

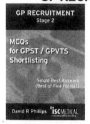